THE CRISIS OF SURVIVAL

Eugene P. Odum
Benjamin DeMott
F. Fraser Darling
John V. Lindsay
Hugh H. Iltis
William Steif
Theodore Berland
William E. Howard
George Wald
Rufus E. Miles, Jr.
David R. Inglis
Ralph Nader
Kenneth E. Boulding
Henry Gibson
Hal Borland
Senator Gaylord A. Nelson
Harold Sprout
Denis Hayes
Gladwin Hill
George F. Kennan
Paul R. Ehrlich
The Editors of *The Progressive*

THE CRISIS OF SURVIVAL

The Editors of *The Progressive*
and the College Division
of Scott, Foresman and Company

with Introductions
by Eugene P. Odum and Benjamin DeMott

Scott, Foresman and Company

Preface

Over the past three decades *The Progressive* magazine has published a series of special issues designed to illuminate major challenges confronting America. In the fall of 1969, the Editors of the magazine, who had published a number of individual articles over the years on the mounting ecological crisis, decided to devote an entire issue to this vital subject. They planned it for the spring of 1970 so that it might make a creative contribution to the National Teach-In on the Environment.

The Editors conferred with a number of experts on the many phases of the challenge to the environment and invited some of the nation's leading authorities to contribute articles to this special issue. The result, seven months in the making, was *The Progressive's* special issue, "The Crisis of Survival."

Scott, Foresman and Company asked to see proofs of the articles while the issue was in preparation. They and their expert consultants quickly came to the conclusion that the material in "The Crisis of Survival" would be of immense value and fill an urgent need for countless Americans if it were also made available in book form. This book, then, is the fruit of our collaboration. Besides the articles in *The Progressive's* Special issue, it includes additional material obtained from such other authorities as distinguished ecologist Eugene Odum, noted critic Benjamin de Mott, statesman George Kennan, and political scientist Harold Sprout. The total presentation is designed to give Americans an authoritative survey of the crisis of the environment and to propose creative alternatives to those present policies leading us so inexorably toward disaster.

The Editors of *The Progressive*
Scott, Foresman's College Division

Contents

Note: Asterisked articles appeared in the April 1970 special issue of *The Progressive*.

Action for Survival

A Prologue by The Editors of *The Progressive*

IN JUNE 1969, *The Progressive* published a special issue entitled "The Power of the Pentagon." In it more than a score of the nation's leading scientists, scholars, and public officials examined the social, political, and moral challenge confronting America. They discussed, documented, and denounced the militarization of our foreign policy and the distortion of our national priorities. They also emphasized the critical need for more hopeful and creative policies and programs for our country.

In April 1970, we published a companion special issue entitled "The Crisis of Survival." In it a dozen or more distinguished authorities examined the challenge to our physical environment. They underscored their anxiety that man and his planet face extinction as a consequence of our mindless abuse and greedy exploitation of nature. But, for all their deep concerns, they are not ecological doomsayers. They beckon us to alternative paths that carry the prospect of hope, not despair; life, not death.

Both special issues of *The Progressive,* each in its own way, are committed to the same goal: the survival of man, but not that alone—the enrichment of life as well.

It may sound apocalyptic to suggest that man and the nature he corrupts are speeding toward extinction. But the harsh reality, as emphasized by many of our hard-headed experts, is that a new Four Horsemen—Overpopulation, Pollution, the Famine of Resources, and Nuclear War—are riding relentlessly on their mission of destruction.

The process of ravaging our planet has been going on for a long time. The obsessive American hunger for growth, more creature comforts, and an ever fatter Gross National Product—no matter how great the price for polluting and pillaging our national heritage—has contributed significantly to the mounting crisis in our segment of the earth. To question the sacred assumption that economic growth is always an unmixed blessing is, as *The Wall Street Journal* noted recently, "to threaten the American dream itself."

But the dream has become a nightmare. A runaway technology, whose only law is profit, has for decades corrupted our air, ravished our soil, denuded our forests, and polluted our water resources. The result is an environment assailed by noxious doses of fumes, sewage, smoke, noise, filth, chemicals, ugliness, and urban decay. And the crisis is compounded by a steadily rising population in defiance of all sense and science.

The worsening crisis commanded little concern until recently. It is one of the more curious phenomena of our time that the subject of our environment is now capturing such extraordinary public interest and concern after these many years of indifference and neglect.

Everyone, it seems, is getting into the act. *Time, Life,* and *Fortune, Newsweek, Esquire,* and *McCall's* are only some of the slicks among the Establishment media which have given splash treatment to the threat to the environment in the past few months. The daily press has poured out a multitude of news stories and editorials to mark its own concern. And the television networks have been competing with a spate of "specials" to announce their arrival at the scene of crisis.

The politicians, not sure whether concern over deterioration of the environment is a craze or a crusade, have elected, predictably, to play it safe. From President Nixon to the local alderman, they have pounced on the issue and commandeered it as the new vehicle of consensus politics. Mr. Nixon, especially, has come rushing forward with a loud "me too" although he never before displayed much concern for the problem. Even now he seems more given to rhetoric than action, and appears none too eager to use the funds and powers he already commands to fight pollution. Since his ecological spree earlier this year, he has resumed his

---

A Sea of Swill

Lake Erie is dead. The beaches at Santa Barbara are deserted. The air in New York is dangerous to breathe. We are drowning in a sea of swill; in a normal year the United States "produces" 142 million tons of smoke and fumes, seven million junked cars, twenty million tons of waste paper, forty-eight billion used cans, and fifty trillion gallons of industrial sewage. And presiding over this rampant process of environmental overloading is the most fearsome reality of all—a population that is still increasing like an uncontrollable cancer on the surface of the globe. I know of no more sobering statistic in this regard than that between now and 1980 the number of women in the most fertile age brackets, eighteen to thirty-two, will double.

ROBERT HEILBRONER
in *Saturday Review*
January, 1970

emphasis on a greater buildup of military hardware, especially ABM and MIRV nuclear missiles.

The polluters, too, want their share of the action. Some of them are buying four-color advertisements in the slicks to assure us that they too love the land and water and woods they go on polluting for profit. Their enthusiasm for the rhetoric of the great environmental crusade does not prevent them from exercising their political clout to soften the penalties for pollution and to dilute enforcement of the many laws, largely unenforced, now on the books. Joseph Wood Krutch, the noted essayist in the environmental field, has told us, for example, about an air pollution ordinance passed in Pima County, Arizona. The ordinance contained an exemption: It does not apply to the copper smelting plants, which are responsible for ninety per cent of the local air pollution.

The sudden and spectacular emergence of the environmental issue poses a host of problems. Perhaps the most important is that involvement in ecological concerns could readily serve—and to some extent may have already served—to divert public attention and the crusading zeal of progressive forces from the continuing tragedy in Vietnam, from an imperialistic foreign policy that invites more Vietnams, from a catastrophic arms race that could gut our planet more rapidly than the many-sided process of pollution, from a callous neglect of persistent poverty and racism in the United States.

These are understandable apprehensions. Former Supreme Court Justice Arthur Goldberg expressed his misgivings when he told the American Association of School Administrators that racial discrimination, poverty amid affluence, urban squalor and decay, and alienation of young people pollute the environment as much as garbage and industrial smoke.

"Unemployment and the alienation of the disadvantaged and the young make for a bad environment," he rightly pointed out. "Garbage and smog pollute our neighborhoods, but hate and prejudice do so in even greater degree. Environmental reform calls imperatively for water and air pollution control, but even more importantly for enhancing educational and job opportunities."

Mr. Goldberg is concerned to have the concept of environmental crisis broadened to include long neglected social and economic problems. This makes great sense to us. To think of cleaning up the environment without emphasizing the social structure at least as much as the physical strikes us as an exercise in self deception. Neither means much without the other. A polluted political system which enables a handful of senile Southerners to dominate, through the seniority system, the law making body of a supposedly free people is a political system which finds racism, poverty, *and* poisoned rivers equally congenial in its scheme of things.

Readers of *The Crisis of Survival* will note the strong emphasis of our contributors on the links between the challenge on the environmental front and these other problems. For example, they cite the war in Vietnam as a major *obstacle* to meeting the environmental crisis. It is significant that such men of science as George Wald, Paul Ehrlich, Barry Commoner, and David Inglis, and men of politics such as Mayor John Lindsay and Senator Gaylord Nelson—all contributors to this issue —are among the country's most outspoken critics of the Vietnam war and of the enormously swollen U.S. military budget. The true ecological crusaders and the peace crusaders have a common objective—a world to save from war, poverty, racism—and pollution.

This objective is poison to right wing forces now contributing to the verbal overkill on the issue of environment while they oppose action programs of basic reform. They view the current environmental movement with good-natured tolerance so long as it languishes in the realm of rhetoric, so long as it goes no farther than it did in the halcyon days when the conservation movement was thought to be in the hands of nature nuts passing out packets of seedlings to Boy Scouts and little old men in overshoes flitting through the forests with their nets hunting for butterflies.

Whatever it may have meant in previous times, conservation today is a grim synonym for survival.

Crusaders for a genuinely fundamental program to clean up the environment will know they are on the right track when the spokesmen for the corporate establishment switch from their present purring approval of something they call conservation to roars of recrimination against those who, in the process of combatting pollution, would disturb their corporate profits and power.

A good sign of the progress achieved thus far by the ecological movement turned up recently in *National Review,* William Buckley's journal for the literates of the Far Right. The magazine hoisted storm signals for its arch conservative readership, warning of the "climate of hysteria that clouds the pollution question," expressing fear that enthusiasm for conservation "can be fashioned into a nasty weapon for those who dislike business on general principles," and snorting at talk that there is "an unavoidable conflict between the 'economy' and the 'environment.' "

We would be lacking in candor if we did not agree that there are discouraging symptoms of faddism—and political opportunism—in the newly regenerated ecological movement. To all the other hazards that peril the environment we must add the danger that it will be talked to death. "Ecology," says California's consummate politician Jess Unruh, "has become the political substitute for the word 'mother.' "

The politics of the environmental movement can be discerned only dimly at the moment. Columnist Joseph Kraft may have been partly right in observing recently: "So far, at least, the politics of environment is very largely the politics of eyewash." But there can be no doubt that the nature of the crisis and the urgency of the challenge are rendering that judgment less accurate every day.

Fortune magazine, in its own special issue on ecology, expressed a view shared by a sizable number of careless observers when it wrote: "For a politician it is the safest of all issues, since conservation has no admitted enemies."

But the politics of survival, as *The Progressive* envisions it, *will* have enemies—powerful enemies. Not surprisingly, many of them will be familiar faces and familiar forces. For the struggle for survival will demand a degree of public spending and public management and control that will constitute a political and social revolution. The confrontation will be between those who are committed to making our presently inadequate social, economic, and political institutions equal to the task of repairing our ravaged environment as against those whose first and enduring allegiance is to private profit and corporate power and the political institutions which stand guard to protect and preserve that profit and power.

So high is the humbug piled on this "safest of all issues" that it is only with the greatest difficulty that even the usually well-informed citizen will be able to find his way in the next few election campaigns. The choice, both within and between parties, will be between those who make speeches and pass resolutions and those who recognize and act upon the fact that time is running out, that only the resolute rejection of war, profits-as-usual, procreation-as-usual, comforts-as-usual, and politics-as-usual will prevent our planet from sliding into disaster. The score cards will be misleading, but you will be able to tell the players by how willing they are to expand public controls designed to combat pollution and other environmental perils, spend the money needed to achieve desperately needed reforms, advocate urgently needed legislation to speed population control, insist on the strictest possible enforcement of anti-pollution laws, impose massive penalties on corporate and individual violators, and propose even stronger measures to stop the wholesale pollution by industry, government, and individuals.

It may be that neither major party will move quickly or boldly enough. The result could be the long talked-about political realignment in America which would enable those who want to clean up our social and economic pollution, as well as the physical environment, to build a great new movement dedicated to striking at the status quo through the instruments of democracy.

If such a new and forward-looking political instrument is forged, it will be the enlightened vanguard of the nation's youth—those who have mastered the methods of democratic action—who will provide much of its dynamism.

The young have been rebelling against an immoral war and unjust social system and a tawdry culture; now they are massing against the polluted physical environment as well. It is to them that we of *The Progressive* dedicate *The Crisis of Survival*—to these, the young, who understand and are prepared to act on this crisis.

catastrophe for all mankind. The book's challenge to the reader is the same as the challenge to society in general, namely, to find the common denominator. I believe that the common denominator is to be found in the concept of the ecological system, or *ecosystem,* which is neither a new nor a radical idea. It is based on the simple fact that the environment of any organism serves as both a "supply depot" and as a "house." Therefore, man is a part of, not apart from, his life support system composed of air, water, minerals, soil, plants, animals, and microorganisms that function together to keep the whole viable. In the past conduct of human affairs, the capacity of the Earth's environment to supply man's physiological and cultural needs and to provide a quality living space, or "Lebensraum," for each individual has been taken for granted, with each of these needs considered a separate and unrelated problem. (Many writers are now pointing out this early unsophisticated view. See especially historian Lynn White's "The historical basis for the ecological crisis," which was first published in *Science* in 1967, and is now widely reprinted.) The dramatic change in people's attitude toward their environment that is now becoming evident stems, I believe, from a general recognition that beyond a certain point the quality of the "Lebensraum" declines drastically as the rate of production and consumption of energy and resources increases, which in turn is a function of the size and affluence of the human population. Consequently, controlled management of the human population and of the environmental life-support components as a single, integrated unit now becomes the greatest, and certainly the most difficult, challenge faced by society.

Since the word "ecology" is derived from a Greek root meaning "house," it is not surprising that the public has adopted this word as a symbol of the totality of man-in-environment. Moreover, the public entry into the "ecology movement" is a natural and predictable response that has been in the making for some time

The danger is that we may no longer have enough time. to complete the task of establishing control over the environment. Also, there is the ever present danger, in times of rapid change, that extreme elements in our society will, either through malice or ignorance, attempt to subvert reform movements and thereby create "backlash" that will delay imperative actions.

Cybernetics, the important new science of control theory, provides a convenient way to view the environmental problem as a whole. In cybernetic language, a system composed of dependent parts that function together can exist in two general states: (1) a "transient" state in which the whole is growing or otherwise changing in time; and (2) a "steady state" in which the system is maintained in equilibrium, a condition of balanced inputs and outputs. For the purposes of our analogy, we can think of the transient state as "youth" and the steady state as "maturity." A growth, or "youthful," stage is under the influence of what is called "positive feedback" in that each increase accelerates another increase, often in geometric progression (a doubling followed by a doubling, etc.). For the individual or the population, as for a new business, growth and positive feedback are necessary for survival. All living organisms and populations have a strong, inherent tendency to grow, born out of the necessity for survival. However, growth does not and cannot continue unrestricted because "negative feedback control" also comes into play, either due to some limitation imposed by the external environment or due to the action of an internal "governor" that brings about an orderly slowdown and establishes a "set point" at which growth stops. As a living system becomes larger and more complex, more of the energy that it transforms must be "fed back" to maintain and control the intricate structure; quality maintenance replaces mere quantitative growth as "the strategy of survival" in the mature system. In summary, then, ultimate survival depends on both positive and negative feedback and on a set-point control mechanism that prevents perturbations from causing damaging oscillations. Many populations of wild animals have evolved a "territorial control behavior" that limits the number of breeding individuals at a level that is optimum for the population, but well below the maximum number that could be supported by the food supply. The articles in this volume strongly indicate that we have begun the search for such a quality control for our own species.

From this brief and elementary discourse on cybernetics, it can be seen that sooner or later transition from youth to maturity must be faced by all levels of life and society, whether they be cells, teenagers, or an ecosystem. Thus, the growth of cells in an organ such as the liver must slow down so as not to exceed the need for maintaining a steady-state function in the mature body. If cell growth does not stop at the maturity of the organ, the results are cancer and the ultimate death of the whole body. So it is with any system of man and nature. What is good, desirable, or adaptive in the youthful stage is often bad, undesirable, or maladaptive in the mature system. For example, very high birth rates, rapid growth, and rampant exploitation of accessible and unused resources are advantageous in a pioneer society, but become disadvantageous in the crowded urban society. Overpopulation can be to society what cancer is to the individual.

As human beings, we do not need to apologize for the fact that we have succeeded in modifying and controlling our natural environment to our collective advantage. We have enjoyed the benefits of positive feedback and have established ourselves on this earth as a highly successful species. However, as the saturation level is approached, and space and resources are all in use, then the exploitive, wasteful approach becomes increasing unadaptive and must be shifted to the opposite pole, to considerations of birth control, for example, or to legalized abortion, recycling and reuse of resources, regulation of land use, complete waste disposal treatment, law and order, civil rights, and the peaceful coexistence of man and nature in general. It is not that our grandfathers did anything wrong. It is just that what was good for grandfather is not appropriate for now. Thus, the meaning of the "ecology movement" is not that we should go back to nature or to grandfather's time; rather, it signifies that we need a new strategy appropriate for today—one that will allow us to "feed back" some of our great power and wealth in order to maintain the quality of the ecosystem. It is fortunate that the young people in this country recognize clearly that their attitudes and goals must be quite different from those of their parents; but the young need guidance in making the necessary smooth transition. Our children will be living in a "full-up" world which requires a different management from that used in the "rapid-growth" world to which we have become accustomed. (See my later contribution to this volume, in which I go into greater detail on the theory of the ecosystem and its relevance to resolving man's conflicts with nature.)

Like all of the great "revolutions in attitude" that have helped to shape and develop society, the need to change man's attitude toward his environment had its early proponents who were long unheeded. In America, the Vermont prophet George Perkins Marsh, in his book Man and Nature written in 1864, analyzed the causes for the decline and fall of ancient civilizations and concluded that environmental abuses were major factors. He forecast a similar doom for modern civilization unless it takes what we would call an "ecosystemic" viewpoint on man and nature. Aldo Leopold, the great American conservationist, wrote nearly forty years ago that "Christianity tries to integrate the individual to society, Democracy to integrate social organization to the individual. There is yet no ethic dealing with man's relation to land ... [which is] still strictly economic, entailing privileges but not obligations" (See "The Land Ethic" in the *Journal of Forestry,* 31: 634–643, 1933;

also widely reprinted in paperback.) "Environmental rights" must now become a part of man's general Bill of Rights.

On the sociological side, William F. Ogburn introduced in the 1920's the concept of the "cultural lag" to indicate that man's attitudes and social customs often do not keep pace with technological developments. Howard W. Odum preferred to think of this tendency in the more positive sense, as an "achievement lag"— meaning that man has too often failed to apply his technical skills to prevent the social problems that have been created by the rapid expansion of technology. H. W. Odum was one of the first to suggest that thorough inventories of man and resources at the local and regional levels should be made and used as bases for national plans of action which would then "integrate" the regions into a coordinated whole. We have come to that now. The articles by Nader and Lindsay in this volume bring out strongly the need to devote massive efforts in support of the consumer and to maintain a quality environment in our cities. The men who maintain our complex machinery and protect our life-support systems must now receive financial rewards and legal protection at least equal to those which we have been accustomed to giving the men who build things and produce goods. The economic and political means of bringing about such a shift in emphasis are discussed by Sprout, Kennan, and Boulding. The ecological parallel has already been mentioned. In nature, the major flow of energy shifts from production to upkeep as the system matures. Ehrlich presents a dramatic view of what might happen if we do not control the "population bomb," while the means of avoiding such a catastrophe are discussed in the Wald and Miles articles.

We can but hope that certain dramatic events which have attracted worldwide attention will shorten the "lag" time between recognition of and action on the environmental crisis. For instance, air pollution in our industrialized urban areas has been widely publicized and serves as a sort of warning light, telling us that a vital system is stressed. It should also shock us into realizing that we have not yet put an economic value on the most vital resource of all, the air, perhaps because our oxogenic atmosphere is created and maintained by organisms other than man.

The trips to the moon have, I am sure, convinced many people that the Earth is more limited and fragile than one might think. As man looked back from the moon through the eyes of the cameras, the planet earth looked not only small, but also unique, since it was the only thing in sight with a beautiful atmosphere capable of supporting human life. It's worth saving.

Introduction

Ecology and Self-Scrutiny: A Cultural Overview

by BENJAMIN DeMOTT

A fresh item, a hot media ticket for the new decade, the "ecology story" has been battered by journalistic cliché almost from the beginning. This newspaper plays the handy Political Angles, separating groundfloor people (Senator Muskie) from me-tooers (President Nixon)

BENJAMIN DeMOTT *is a novelist, teacher, and noted critic of contemporary American art and culture. His most recent book is* Supergrow: Essays and Reports on Imagination in America.

and noting that the cause makes "strange bedfellows" (Girl Scouts, Weathermen, and John Birchers singing the self-same antipollution blues). That one digs the Personalities—"dedicated, hornrimmed" Barry Commoner, "outdoorsy, glamour-puss" David Brower. . . . And everywhere pseudo-events are laid on for electronic newsmen (car burials, Earth Days, and the like)— items occasioning "major speeches," "photographic essays," "public affairs specials," rocking the issue to the beat of Now.

Yet despite the energies expended on conventionalizing and "trivializing" the discovery of the abuse of nature, the thing isn't going under. It has already begun working its way through the bread-and-circus scene of "fastbreaking news" information, entertainment, The Latest. And the evidence at hand testifies that it cannot fail to rank, before long, as a crucial influence on the deep structure of men's inward thought and feeling.

As goes without saying, the influence of the discoveries in question could stop well short of that impact and still be no negligible force. In the world of teaching and learning, for instance, the focus on survival has underlined both the urgency and the mutual interdependence of pedagogical themes often separately teased and deprecated by the knowing in the recent past. Professor Commoner argues that "You can't look at turbidity in a stream intelligently without having some knowledge about the banks of the stream and the forest that's growing twenty-five yards away." And, as the *New York Times* environmental correspondent observes regarding developments in university ecology action centers, awareness of this truth has encouraged the replacement of "the closed-shop compartmentalization of the traditional 'disciplines'—such as biology, chemistry, physics, botany, and geology—[with] an eclectic approach." Support for interdisciplinary work has in turn nourished the cause of "experiential education"—studies that move out from classroom and library situations into the field, confronting the social and political (as well as natural) intricacies of immediate experience. And the result has been the reanimation of an educational ideal to which nobody but lowly commencement speakers have given lipservice for decades: The Whole Man, the scholar-citizen determined not only to know but to connect his knowledge with the moral imperatives of community concern. Doubtless the dignity and interconnectedness of these themes should always have been ungrudgingly granted. But it wasn't, and the rehabilitation of the themes ranks high among the significant visible, public consequences of the environmental revolution thus far.

But the visible public effects of that revolution on nonacademic minds are, of course, far more momentous. The most obvious of the latter has been the intensification, throughout the general culture, of belief in the uniqueness of the age—its discontinuity with yesterday, its character as a period without precedent. Rhetorical public utterances have, true enough, played a part in persuading men of this uniqueness. Denis Hayes, the national coordinator of Environmental Action declares that:

> America is the new Robber Baron. . . . America has become indifferent to life. . . . If 50,000 people are killed, if ten million starve, if an entire country is laid waste—we have learned to tuck the information into the proper file and write the affair off as a mistake.

The editors of *The Progressive* declare in the prologue to this book that "a new Four Horsemen . . . are riding relentlessly on their mission of destruction." The *Saturday Review* warns that:

> Lake Erie is dead. The beaches at Santa Barbara are deserted. The air in New York is dangerous to breathe. We are drowning in a sea of swill; in a normal year the United States produces 142 million tons of smoke

and fumes, seven million junked cars, twenty million tons of waste paper, forty-eight billion used cans, and fifty trillion gallons of industrial sewage . . . a population that is still increasing like an uncontrollable cancer on the surface of the globe.

Paul Ehrlich, the Stanford biologist, presents horrific scenarios for the future:

SCENARIO III. In 1974 the United States government finally realizes that the food-population balance in much of Asia, Africa, and South America is such that most areas cannot attain self-sufficiency. American expeditionary forces are withdrawn from Vietnam and Thailand, and the United States announces it will no longer send food to India, Egypt, and some other countries which it considers beyond hope. A moderate food rationing program is instituted in the United States. It further announces that food production will be increased only so long as the increase can be accomplished without damage to the environment of the North American continent. . . . Famine and food riots sweep Asia. In China, India, and other areas of Asia, central governments weaken and then disappear. . . . Most of the countries of Africa and South America slide backward into famine and local warfare. . . . In the United Nations, the United States, Canada, Russia, Japan, Australia, and the Common Market countries set up a machinery for "area rehabilitation" which will involve simultaneous population control, agricultural development, and limited industrialization, to be carried out jointly in select sections in Asia, Africa, and South America. The plan is to be initiated in 1985, when it is calculated that the major die-back will be over, using famine relief stations as bases for both facilities and personnel. . . .

If the voices addressing ecological crises spoke only in such tones, the present sense of living in an "incomparable" historical moment, might be less widely diffused than it is: Tonal extremism, in the defense of truth, can be an incitement to skepticism. But many spokesmen for the ecological cause say their piece moderately, coolly—yet nevertheless press just as firmly the point that mankind cannot have known an equivalent crisis before. Professor Commoner speaks flatly in *Science and Survival* (1966): "As a biologist, I have reached this conclusion: we have come to a turning point in the human habitation of the earth." The UN Secretary-General, U Thant, matches Commoner's sobriety with his own: "For the first time in the history of mankind, there is arising a crisis of worldwide proportions involving developed and developing countries alike—the crisis of human environment. . . . It is becoming apparent that if current trends continue, the future of life on earth could be endangered." Professor Kenneth Boulding, the economist, remarks—in the course of his own effort at characterizing differences between "then" and now—that "neither the American, nor the French, nor the Russian revolutions created fundamental changes in the state of man [as the present situation has done], and the ideologies which supported [those revolutions] are quite inadequate to bear the weight of this enormous transition which we face. . . ." In short, certainty that the face of the age stares straight into an Absolute Unknown echoes and reechoes throughout the new ecological literature, and can't be discounted as self-hyping hysteria.

If there were nothing more in the equation than this certainty, tracking the cultural impact of the environmental cause back to substantive realities in individual human feeling would be less difficult and less troubling. The point of rest would be—once again— the famous generation gap: The prime change effected in the feeling-life of men might seem a simple matter of new strains on the sympathy and confidence between youth and age. "Awareness of ecological crisis as a wholly new fact of life—a fact of which older generations could not conceivably have a sound grasp—confirmed the thesis of Dr. Margaret Mead that a reversal of generational roles, establishing the young as teachers and the aged as pupils, was the characteristic mark of the times." A formula of that sort could serve well enough to bring primary cultural dimensions into view.

But, as it happens, that formula is inadequate. For the most important human and psychological consequences of the environmental revolution lie not in restructured generational relationships, but, instead, in the extraordinary demand that this revolution lays upon men of every age to achieve detachment from self and culture. The demand in question isn't usually formulated, to be sure, in these terms. Confronted with the task of explaining what is necessary for survival, the leaders of the cause seldom speak first of detachment. Professor Commoner calls for a new means of salvation: "This, I believe, is the urgency of the environmental crisis—we must determine, now, to develop, in the next decade, the new means of our salvation." The *Times'* Gladwin Hill speaks of the need for a rebellion —"a sudden, remarkable, spontaneous rebellion not of one group against another so much as of everybody against the physical conditions to which two centuries of promiscuous 'progress' have brought us. . . ." And the head of the Rockefeller Foundation, Dr. George Harrar, plumps for a "new environmental ethic."

But implicit in every address to the problem (and explicit in most) is the requirement that men raise to the level of consciousness myths, values, profound unexamined assumptions governing Western attitudes toward life—in a word, that they teach themselves to objectify their culture. "There appears to be only one viable approach," according to the editors of the Population Bulletin:

> This is the long uphill route of encouraging the American people to modify their basic attitudes and behavior so that instead of idealizing large families in the abstract and creating them in flesh and blood, we will prefer small ones and act upon our preferences; so that instead of promoting forms of economic

growth which will increasingly pollute our living space, we will insist that we clean up as we go, no matter what the cost; so that instead of measuring our welfare by the amount of our consumption, we will become deeply concerned about enhancing the quality and preserving the variety of life in the momentum of our society.

Can the task of "modifying basic attitudes" begin until "basic attitudes" are laid out to plain view? Is there any way of carrying this work through without disentangling the "attitudes" from their tight relationships with every sector of the belief system, excising layers of inexpressible myth and symbol, objectifying them, hypostatizing them? It's common, as might be expected, for leaders advocating exactly this step to speak as though the job were more or less routine—no need for anxiety or bitter wounds of self. "At this critical juncture," says Dr. Harrar equably, "it would be well for man to question the validity of his attitudes toward nature and to consider seriously the desirability and wisdom of formulating a new ethic for dealing with his natural environment which would transcend most of the values we have traditionally held concerning the world." And Senator Nelson states the need in a comfortably positive voice:

> Restoring our environment and establishing quality on a par with quantity as a goal of American life would require a reshaping of our values, sweeping changes in the performance and goals of our institutions . . . a humanizing and redirection of our technology. . . . There is a great need and growing support for the introduction of new values in our society. . . .

But here and there among the ecological spokesmen, a few writers are awed by the very conception of a "transformation of values." (Professor Boulding speaks of the "enormous intellectual and moral task which lies ahead of mankind.")

And even if such people didn't exist, the scope and nature of the work wouldn't be hidden from us. For the case is, as all readers of literature and students of history know, that the public voices now charging us to remake culture and personhood are far from speaking a new tongue. The voice of anger against the dehumanization of the Earth has resounded in letters and philosophy for longer than two centuries. The great protest on behalf of the organic view of nature that Professor Whitehead heard in the romantic poets has been a ground-theme of literature from the "romantic movement" to the present. The will to criticize the industrial civilization, to view its gifts as ambiguous, to oppose the despoliation of the landscape, is a norm everywhere in American literature from Hawthorne to Fitzgerald and after (see the invaluable work of Professor Leo Marx in this area). "Civilization" has been understood as in process of destroying itself by virtually every major English writer from Blake to Lawrence, and the need for "a new ethic" has been urged by scores of writers contributing, over the past century, to the debate about culture and society in that country. Nor is the story different on the Continent. The profound injunction to know one's cultural inheritance and distrust it, to fight free of it, to seek some original encounter with experience, sloughing off bourgeois and other forms, has been the staple stuff of existential thought from its beginnings. "You must change your life," cries the poet Rilke—and it is precisely that command that has now become the keyword of the party of survival.

But obeying it means suffering—and men are beginning to grasp this truth. Steadily, ever more clearly, men are coming to understand that what they were doing was wrong, that what they have been, they must now begin to cease to be, that what their children are to become cannot flow from what they, the parents, have set before them as The Good, and that in discontinuity and interruption lie not disaster but the single ground of a habitable future. These new understandings link up, in psychological terms, with those inspired by the other major domestic event of this age—the discovery of the black man's experience. The latter discovery raised the question whether the obliviousness of our fathers to the suffering and inhumanity endured by millions of black men in their midst did not invalidate history, precedent, and "accepted moral tradition" as guides to behavior. Who could believe in the significance or dignity of such an uncaring past?

And the impact of the discovery of the abuse of nature—the ecological crisis—is to intensify that question, while extending the area of doubt from history to the self. For the crisis of survival doesn't simply call into question once more the worth of respected institutions, or the gospel of success, or the bootstrap myth, or the sanctity of abundance, technological revolution "laborsaving devices," automation, "economic order," and the rest. It challenges the conception of personal development and self-realization that has governed Western culture for centuries, established its sense of public and private priorities, given it its deepest understanding of crime and of virtue, taught it the terms on which history can be regarded as purposeful.

What will come of this challenge? It will either attain full potency, men say, ultimately interposing a barrier between spaceship earth and those forces of ego-ridden greed that have willed a "world wasteland"—or it will be overmatched, smothered, borne down by the counterpressures of social myth, habit, stereotype. In the balance of the context hangs survival.

This account of our situation, as set forth in the book in your hand, is impressive and believable. Yet, it is perhaps not, and doubtless was not intended to be, a complete guide to the human realities lying just ahead. What it cannot body forth is the character of that inner human experience—the quality of the new self—upon which hope now rests. It is one thing to say we must learn to "doubt our values," strive to become critical of our culture, and another to imagine the desiderated state of mind from within. We are asked, in the name of survival, to become our own witnesses, to see ourselves from outside, to turn against "bourgeois values," to sit like Harry Haller in Hasse's story of a lone wolf and gaze down the stairs at the neat plants in our middle-class hallways, at our cleanliness, our dutifulness, our high-gloss responsibility, our rectitude as hitherto understood—we are asked to gaze at all this and read it finally as error and deceit and corruption. (The problem says Professor Boulding, is that

> "Nobody has solved the problem of how to prevent the insidious corruption both of the culture of the powerful and the culture of the impotent.")

Our task, in sum, is to teach ourselves to become, man by man, woman by woman, each the agent of his own dismantling—his own movement on from a received "cultural self" to an unknown new identity. And to perform the task, we must forego familiar gratifications. Against the greed that chokes our air we pit the prod of self-analysis, but not the hope of self-approval, the untender energies of self-critique, but not the fantasies of reconciliation. For—to speak in an extreme tone—it cannot be repeated too often: *What we have been we must now cease to be.* There appears no alternative save that of extricating ourselves from our current path. Our devotion to dissociated self- and culture-watching, self-sponsored disintegration of unifying cultural myths and symbols, must be total. And it is precisely here—in the command to uncreate ourselves—that the deepest cultural meanings of this crisis come into view. We are at a moment in history when the quest for the freedom of love, the dream of full self-acceptance—release from the experience of rejection, repudiation, prohibition—is no longer affordable. Salvation as alienation, complacency as suicide, security as self-doubt—these are the new laws, seemingly, of personal balance and wholeness. The truth implicit stands well beyond melodrama, yet is expressible only in melodramatic terms: Men have come close to their own borders; they are nearing the severest tests yet known of human nerve.

A Wider Environment of Ecology and Conservation

by F. FRASER DARLING

Pierre Dansereau's first of twenty-seven propositions or laws of ecology has the shattering simplicity of great thoughts. His Law of the Inoptimum says, "No species encounters in any given habitat the optimum conditions for all of its functions." Few ecologists give sufficient heed to this dictum when studying the life

---

Eminent in the field of ecology, F. FRASER DARLING *is also a leader of the Conservation Foundation. He has written many books, including* The Unity of Ecology.

From: Daedalus, *Vol. 96, No. 4, (Fall 1967): 1003-1019, with deletions. Reprinted by permission of* Daedalus, *Journal of the American Academy of Arts and Sciences, Boston, Massachusetts.*

history of any single species, though it glimmers through when a whole community or biome is being considered. Most earnest workers for the supposed welfare of man have never heard of the Law of the Inoptimum and would scarcely be ready to believe it anyway. Yet Dansereau has given us the perfect text for that desirable state of being for all those who delve into the ground of living things and their environment—namely, the state of unembittered disillusion.

Ecology, as the science of the organism in relation to its environment and of the relations between communities of organisms of like or different kinds, was a bigger idea than the initiators grasped. The beauty of the idea was in its bigness and readiness to cross boundaries, looking into less well understood fields than one's own and finding links, correlations, comparisons, contrasts, and differences of exquisitely fine scale and subtlety.

The botanists did the first critical work that set a standard. Animal ecology followed rather hesitantly. In 1927, at the age of twenty-seven, Charles Elton published *Animal Ecology,* a landmark in this field because it expresses, almost without saying so, a philosophy, a vision of complexity in which the behavior of animals is itself a factor in the environment of others. He asked that botanists and other scientists cooperate in coming to an understanding of how communities coexist. "The movement of the moon or of a dog's tail or the psychology of starlings" was a matter of significance; answers were not in books. Julian Huxley's introduction to the volume saw clearly the social implications that ecology would have; that all applied biology would need to shed its *ad hoc* approach, such as thinking of the elimination of a "pest," and seek guiding principles in pure and applied ecology. We now understand that a "pest" is an indicator of environmental imbalance.

Elton's contribution to ecological theory has been progressive and massive. His latest book, *The Pattern of Animal Communities,* gives us guidelines for the future. This book represents twenty years of research by

Elton and his graduate students on a small wooded landscape at Whytham Hill, near his university and home. Our mobile academic world is producing too few of such studies, when they are so much needed. . . .

Wholeness in approach has been carried through in Elton's book in beautiful detail, but with a leisured, philosophical quietness and literary quality that can be deceptive. The key has been the handling of large amounts of data without losing track of their validity or meaning. In this larger field, the early American contributions of Homer Shantz, primarily a botanist, and Aldo Leopold, the philosophic founder of the study of wildlife management, were very great indeed and redound to the credit of a hardheaded but imaginative governmental agency, the U.S. Forest Service, and its first head, Gifford Pinchot.

Shantz, in my mind, was the exponent of the biotic factor, for he saw examples of the interaction of vegetational cover and animal life wherever he went and found youthful enjoyment in each facet he discovered. In 1923, he journeyed from Cairo to the Cape with C. F. Marbut and produced a vegetational atlas that stood for thirty years. As an indefatigable photographer, he took a series of photographs of all he saw. This proved its value spectacularly in 1956 when he repeated the journey and took a new series of photographs from as near the same points as possible. The before-and-after pictures were published by the University of Arizona and backed up Shantz's scrupulous observations. (Shantz showed me the link between the antelope ground squirrel and that important desert browse plant, bitterbush: Single seeds do not germinate and survive in nature, whereas the forgotten caches of seeds of these little rodents do germinate as a group, though only one plant will survive the shortage of water.) Shantz enjoyed the dynamic interacting world of natural history; he saw that it made sense. Leopold was deeply influenced by the deserts of New Mexico and Arizona and what people were doing to the land.

I suppose there is no philosopher who does not suffer, and Leopold reflected, "One of the penalties of an eco-logical education is that one lives alone in a world of wounds. Much of the damage inflicted on land is invis-ible to laymen."

He, too, saw wholes and grappled with them, as his book *Game Management,* published in 1933, shows. His greatest contribution, however, was his struggle for a land ethic of conservation based on impeccable scientific principles.

> When we see land as a community to which we belong, we may begin to use it with love and respect. There is no other way for land to survive the impact of mech-anized man, nor for us to reap from it the aesthetic harvest it is capable, under science, of contributing to culture.
>
> That land is a community is the basic concept of ecol-ogy, but that land is to be loved and respected is an ex-tension of ethics. That land yields a cultural harvest is a fact long known, but latterly often forgotten.

If this attitude of mind is held at all, I would say it is an ecological factor affecting the world environment and a proper stage in our own development of awareness.

There are obvious limits to the breadth and depth of any man's science. Thus, early ecology, which looked far and wide, drew pursed lips from the purists and those to whom research meant learning more and more about less and less. The ecologists made mistakes, but they could be faultless and fearless in the scientific principles—old truths really—they were unearthing like archaeological treasures. Ecology was stimulating, with-out being particularly rewarding of ambition in the profession of science. . . .

Inevitably, specialization has taken place. It was nec-essary to have such fine analysis for the larger synthesis, but to what extent are we prepared now to step forth into the world of men and its psychological dimension? Ecologists have resisted the notion of human ecology,

in much the same way that earlier plant ecologists neglected biotic influences on plant communities. Shantz
and Leopold cut right through this sophistry in their
studies of the overgrazed western ranges. The geogra-
pher Carl Sauer always saw ecology in the larger terms
of human activity, as his early study of the Ozark region
shows. This was also my own approach in *West High-
land Survey*. There is only one ecology.

Nevertheless, there has been a further tendency on
the part of ecologists to turn inward and to exclude,
when their science demands outward vision. The governmental and administrative world, even the commercial world, has heard of ecology. The idea—or at least
the word—is liked, for we hear it generally bandied
about, but are ecologists demonstrating that their science has a continuing stream from the academic watershed to the complexity of the estuary with its people
and its pollution? Physicists, chemists, and mathema-
ticians are conscious of their streams of permeation.
Ecology as a profession arrived belatedly and has not
yet devised its means of communication.

A [1966] conference drew together a small group of
ecologists, economists, architects, planners, lawyers,
publicists, and a physician to discuss the subject of the
future environments of North America. As one of the
ecologists present, I felt our science seemed unable to
rise to its opportunity. Some of us expressed the need
for much deeper research before anything definite could
be said; others put forward as prosposals for study space
and material that the group thought unrealistic. The
ecologists were fine idealists, and their philosophy was
unexceptionable. Finally, they came out with truths
which the company warmly accepted, but before then
that ecologically sympathetic economist Kenneth
Boulding had said, "You do not have any sophisticated
knowledge in ecology. Ecology, as far as I can see, has
been one of the most unsophisticated of the sciences.
You are a bunch of bird-watchers. You really are."

Boulding spoke surer than he knew, for out of the

nest of bird-watchers have come some of those ecologists who have essayed the furthest forward. At the risk of being invidious, I would mention William Vogt, who did more [and did it earlier] to shock the world into consciousness of the human population problem than anyone else; and Max Nicholson, who at twenty-one wrote a book on avian economics, *How Birds Live,* and who, since then, has founded the research organization, Political and Economic Planning, and has been Director-General of the Nature Conservancy, a British government agency.

What Boulding was thinking and what made me uncomfortable that day was the ecologists' apparent inability to make constructive proposals in the face of specific and urgent problems. . . . The auditor of a balance sheet has a form of statement that safeguards his signature; the ecologist should be no more fearful nor diffident.

Such a meticulous worker as Derrick Ovington cautions that we know too little and that ecology cannot answer with authority the questions asked of it. He pleads for more time in research. By concentrating his work on the breakdown and recycling of detritus in woodlands, he is building some accurate notion of primary and secondary productivity in this kind of ecosystem. Edward Deevey has been doing the same sort of work in fresh-water systems; the Odum brothers and Larry Slobodkin have almost produced a revolution in ecology by their quantitative work in recycling of nutrients, while C. Overgaard Nielson and H. Ellenberg have been doing similar work in Europe. All these workers are either bound up with the International Biological Program or its study of the productivity of Biological systems. From the academic side of ecology, they employ difficult technical methods and imaginatively adapt techniques from other sciences to their work. These scholars are representative of the fundamental research we can hope will be supported and enlarged to give us the basic reasoning for ultimate social application.

The concept of the ecosystem or biome as the unit is quite clear, but it would remain philosophical and speculative unless the involved laboratory work on the detailed nature of conversion cycles is developed further. The long-term program of the Nature Conservancy, one of the largest in this field in the world, recognizes this quite clearly. It has been reckoned that over two thousand man-years have already gone into fundamental research and that management of nature reserves and land-use ecology in general are now having some meaning. These scholars are not bird-watchers but bricklayers.

The preservation of samples of the planet's natural areas is no supine task of designation, acquisition, and thereafter letting be. Rather, it requires having such an understanding of the dynamic nature of the plant and animal communities and of the physical and social interaction of environmental factors that knowledgeable regulatory action can be taken before irrevocable change impinges. When Elton discussed his concept of *niche* in ecology in 1927, he stressed the functional quality of an organism in its habitat. The wolverine in the Arctic and the hyena in the tropical environment were filling the same niche, being the bone-grinding kind of scavenger. This is a graphic expression of a principle now comprehended more fully in the study of ecosystems: In short, organisms exploit their environment to their best advantage and contribute unconsciously to the ideal of non-loss of energy from the ecosystem as a whole and, at the same time, to the maintenance of the maximum active flow of energy through the ecosystem. . . .

Ecology no longer has to bother about academic respectability, and it should face firmly its social destiny. To some extent, conservation has been applied ecology or ecology in action, but, in general, the ecologist is nervous in the company of the devotee of conservation. The idea of conservation is easy and emotionally satisfying, and the half-bake finds himself in a mutual-admiration society. Without much difficulty, this kind of conservationist can believe he is a superior sort of person, which boosts his ego. It is all very trying, yet our greatest ecologists are in the front ranks of the Conservation Movement with all its shortcomings; they rise above academic diffidence and are ready to accept the social destiny of their science. Moreover, they are helping us to think of many administrative and political problems in ecological terms. . . . Paul Sears, Fairfield Osborn, Marston Bates, and Raymond Dasmann [and others] have written books with direct social impact. Sears's *Deserts on the March* and Osborn's *Our Plundered Planet* were early classics that made some worldwide difference, but I have an uncomfortable feeling that several good books published since then have been treated as "scare" literature. It behooves every writer of these necessary pieces to prune his English. The facts do not need the big drum.

Politics, let us admit, is an immensely important ecological factor on this planet. Perhaps howler monkeys show the rudiments of political tribalism, but otherwise man is the unique political animal. To this unique characteristic is linked man's ability to lie to himself and be believed. These aspects of animal behavior influence the ecology of our planet and have done so throughout history. The notion of biopolitics, while not new, is capable of immense development even in one's own mind before it reaches action. Nations, like ecosystems, tend toward complexity, which, at its best, means efficiency in energy flow. As each organism evolves, it must find its own niche and survive by natural selection. If we liken a nation to an ecosystem, have we an interlocking community of institutions furthering energy flow within itself or an agglomeration of almost random organizations (that is, organisms) operating without natural selection, without a definite trend toward integration and establishment of a niche structure? Both nation and ecosystem are in a state of process: Losses are suffered and can be adjusted by adaptation and, in the same way, introductions can be taken into the system. Occasionally, either loss or introduction might wreck the ecosystem or the civilization.

Our proliferations of institutions have not yet become integrated as an ecosystem. Our communication is imperfect, and we must deal with loyalties and egos. G. F. Gause's axiom states that if two species occupy the same niche-function in the same habitat, one will eventually become dominant and replace the other. This kind of thinking is necessary as an ecological attitude in our management of bear gardens. Political economy needs the ecologist who can apply himself without becoming a politician.

I look upon Lynton Caldwell as the leading thinker in biopolitics. He is a political economist who has realized the possible fruitfulness of the borderline areas between sciences. Leopold used to talk about "edge effects," the richness of natural history on the borders of habitats. The academic ecologist speaks of the *ecotone,* and Caldwell is examining one of these areas in administrative possibilities for environmental control. His book, *Biopolitics: Science, Ethics and Public Policy,* was published in 1964, but has taken too long to get through to general comprehension. The White House Conference on Natural Beauty, held in 1965, was perhaps a turning point, because it clarified an enlarged concept of public responsibility and administrative innovation, the keynote of Caldwell's biopolitics. President [Johnson], in his Message on Natural Beauty, said:

> Our conservation must not be just the classic conservation of protection and development, but a creative conservation of restoration and innovation. Its concern is not with nature alone but with the total relation between man and the world around him.

[President Nixon, too, is acting on this thesis.]
Caldwell writes:

> Politics in the broad sense operates through the administrative process as well as outside of it, and is one of the fibers that tie together the internal and external aspects of public administration, giving it functional coherence. The character of administrative action often reveals the extent to which this coherence has been achieved in politics, and can be expressed in public policy.

In short, public policy has to be ahead of popular consensus, which is often confused, even when informed action is crucial. . . .

Conservation as ecology in action is indeed looking outward from its traditional field of nature. Speeches by Russell Train, Raymond Dasmann, [and others] have spelled out conservation's concern with planning and the phenomenon of urbanism. Urbanism is one facet of the increase of human population with which ecology is already involved. But advancing urbanism also implies rural regression, an area in which conservation can offer special help. The mobility provided by the internal combustion engine has made possible the leaping urban sprawl so different from the medieval, intensely urban city with its sharply defined country of fields and woods. More, however, is involved than the mere non-beauty of urban sprawl. Rural life has many disciplines that have survival value for the community and its land. The fracture these undergo as they fall increasingly within the penumbra of modern semi- and sub-urbanism can have sharp ecological consequences that may be apparent even in psychosomatic manifestations in the population.

We know little about the human environment, and its complexity does not lend itself to full analysis because subjective values of widely varying character are concerned. Indeed, many human environments are speciated by their subjective values. Social anthropology and sociology are directly concerned with such analysis, but ecology can fill a very obvious gap. The ecology of

stress in human communities and environments immediately demonstrates the truth of Dansereau's first law.
The unembittered *désillusioné,* who finds no place for
rose-colored spectacles, does not foster the impulse to
create the perfect environment nor to bring the human
being to the encapsulated state of homeostasis that can
only be imaginary and never real. But analysis of the
environment is worth trying, and the ecologist should
not avoid considering subjective values ecological factors. Early construction of superhighways naturally
favored the straight line, but drivers tended to fall
asleep on them; some curving and landscaping are now
normal at some extra engineering cost. Diversity, be it
ever so little, has value in relieving stress. As we urban-
ize, the green leaf is becoming increasingly important
to our content and well-being. The eastern forest of the
United States, which has little or no timber value and
a rapidly declining significance for fuel supplies, is ap-
proaching its zenith of service to mankind as the sub-
urban forest, the pleasance of the people.

Psychosomatic diseases are a manifestation of varied
patterns of environmental conditions bearing on persons of different habitus types. These diseases may be
alleviated by drugs or surgery, but their radical cure
depends on removing stress conditions. Habitus type
may well determine whether the expression of the psychosomatic ill is a duodenal ulcer, asthma, migraine,
lumbago, or cardiac disease. It is imperative that physicians inclined toward ecology take part in the investigation of the human environment. Pure water and pure
air are accepted as being desirable, but the nature of
the environment is too little considered. Uncontrolled
"development" instigated largely by economic motives
is prodigal and destructive of what could be desirable
human habitat. Tactile and visual repose should be
considered by engineers and builders, and the ecologist
could help if he devoted some research time now. Curving lines, trees and their textures, masses and seasonal
variation, the place of water still and in motion—these

things may be impractical, but so much of human pleasure is impractical. . . . The so-called rise in the standard of living is being attended by a definite lowering of the standard of living in environmental terms. Silence or absence of cacophony is a scarce commodity; the simple peasant fare of home-baked brown bread and freshly made butter can be enjoyed only by the very rich in Western society.

We find these factors difficult to analyze, yet the ecologist can join with the physician and the psychologist in helping the planner and the landscape architect. Ian McHarg, of the University of Pennsylvania, has emphasized the place of ecology in landscape architecture and practiced the idea in the Delaware River project. Unfortunately, expression and practice of this kind of ecology and continuing research demand a present prosperity of high order in a society that has neglected public beauty and amenity for so long. Wars cut very deep into the surplus that could be applied to environmental research and experimentation. The tendency then is to make do in an environment that is steadily deteriorating ecologically. . . .

All of us are aware of the rapid change in our environment, and how projected changes can be brought to the stage of "starting on Monday morning" before the citizen is aware of them. The public hearing is precipitated, and any ecological evidence offered is hurried in its preparation and unimpressive. At rather less short notice, come the announcements of intended dams, about which the public can have its say. The Wilderness Society, the Sierra Club, and the National Parks Association in the United States do a splendid job in guarding the nation's heritage, often using sound ecological arguments, but the ecologists themselves might well maintain through their societies an intelligence center, making them more ready to serve the public. An excellent example of good ecological reconnaissance and subsequent presentation of a report of immense strength was the effort by Dean Spurr's team which examined the Rampart Dam proposal on the Yukon. The deduced consequences of the dam were worked through with the utmost scientific integrity, completely devoid of bias or special pleading. (Several societies had asked for this survey and collectively paid for it.) . . .

Ecologists might conduct surveys methodologically similar to the "scenarios" of the Hudson Institute. There, imaginary military debacles are set forth, including the hypothetical dropping of atomic bombs of certain weights on certain places. The consequences are followed through in considerable ecological detail by the time the scenario is presented. Ecologists could learn much from this technique, and the cases they could work on would not be nearly so imaginary. . . .

In the same line of thought, ecological reconnaissance can be developed further to give a fairly accurate, reasonably quick answer to specific problems. The ecologist cannot expect to be taken seriously in public affairs if he constantly takes refuge behind the need for more research. If he has kept himself aware of the width of his subject and used the ecologist's special aptitude, natural and developed, for comparative observation, he will have gained a shrewd notion of indicators that may themselves be single species of plants or animals, types of growth, or combinations of these. One of the pioneers of "short cuts" in ecological reconnaissance has been Thane Riney.... The Sierras of California were his nursery when he worked on the mule deer; he then spent seven years in the steep country of South Island in New Zealand, and he traveled extensively throughout most of Africa. Even the press of the heel into the ground can indicate much to the trained observer. The art and science of rapid, accurate reconnaissance must surely be one of the developments in academic ecology in the future, though in my opinion not enough attention is being paid to it in training curricula. The need is great in all countries. Immense areas of the so-called developed countries (I prefer the truer word, *overdeveloped*), as well as the developing countries, need the scrutiny of an ecological survey. Such reconnaissance gives us a notion of carrying capacity, to use the agronomist's phrase. The ecologist would use it in a wider sense, perhaps the weight and incidence of flat feet in national parks, the year to year density of snowy owls on an Arctic tundra, or the balance of the wide spectrum of grazing and browsing animals on an African savannah. Riney has brought the word *syndrome* into ecological use in recognizing the composite ills of land in nature.

The airplane has proved to be a boon for the ecologist. Other sciences quickly took advantage of this tool, and two world wars provided breakthroughs in the interpretation of aerial photographs that have been immensely useful to the ecologist since 1945....

Nothing equals the value of carefully slanted aerial photographs in census work on certain birds and mammals. The method is suspect, however, for some creatures that do not make themselves evident even though they are above ground. Excellent combined plant and animal ecological studies have been done for the wilder lands, such as Alaska and Africa, but what has gone before seems elementary to what is hoped for in the future. Remote sensors and photogrammetry promise extraordinary detail and accuracy; satellite and radar photographs can be used for estimating environmental change and land-use patterns in places we cannot reach.

These special techniques borrowed from other sciences will make possible much deeper intellectual penetration of study areas and provide quickly a mass of data. Mathematics has already served ecology well through the work of Lotka, Bodenheimer, Solomon, Nicholson, Leslie, and, more recently, Martin Holgate, who is also an ecologist. Mathematics will now play a larger role in testing and interpreting data, for the plain descriptive ecologist will increasingly seek the specialist aid of the mathematician.

Ecology has also borrowed from gas chromatography its means of selective detection of pesticide residues and metabolites. The use of pesticides has been a subject of heated public controversy, and some rather uncritical work has been done on these compounds in relation to wildlife conservation. Pesticides have damaged the environment, but the extent and nature of this damage have not yet been satisfactorily determined. The practices used by commercial firms in determining effects and safety factors are very deficient. Commerce cannot afford the time to get the results the ecologist would consider adequate. The ecologist, on the other hand, is called upon to be accurate for field conditions, rather than for laboratory experimentation. The answer is an anticlimax if the endangered species is by then extinct. The new selective-detection techniques may save the ecologist's face in this field as well as precious time.

The practice of using pesticidal compounds in the last quarter of a century has certainly brought the ecologist nearer to his social role.... I would emphasize that the interdisciplinary approach to ecological problems is now essential. The ecologist is less likely to be the lone naturalist who observes and contemplates than a member of a team that is able to draw on diverse disciplines.

The pesticide problem has also triggered much fundamental ecological research on population dynamics, whether of soil fauna or American robins. Thus, monitoring systems on indicator organisms—man, bird, and mollusk—are being made possible. Monitoring itself is in line with the "scenario" technique. It attempts to supply us not only with contemporary knowledge but with forecasts of future trends—both of which ecology needs for prompt, active, and effective social participation.

Pollution of the environment is a product of our age, resulting from increase of human population, from technological activity, and from the linked phenomenon of urbanization. At the moment we are losing the battle for man's sense of well-being. Ecology and conservation have much to offer and discover. By their future concern and involvement with the human species and its environment, they will serve no less well the field of nature where they have worked heretofore.

The burden of this essay has been the breadth of concern of ecology and conservation. Is the field of endeavor to become so diffuse that we become all-embracing, utterly superficial, and lightweight? There is this danger, but I do not think Caldwell, Cooley, Fosberg [and like men] will fall into it. They are men of different skills, expressing similar ideas. Proponents of the ecological approach with this breadth of skills can talk the same language, and such communication produces the rich dynamism of "edge effects." This interaction may be the ecologist's salvation. If specialists can be outward-looking as well and ecologists can communicate with them quickly, breadth of front can be deep also. Then ecologists will be able to take their place at the council table as socially conscious people capable of adjustment and compromise in a complex world where politics is a major ecological factor in the total environment.

The Plight
of the Cities

by JOHN V. LINDSAY

THE DEGRADATION of the environment is by now a familiar story: polluted air and water, a decaying physical plant, massive sanitation problems, sharp rises in congestion and noise that bring tension, lost efficiency, and incivility.

We are suffering from the mistakes of decades. Poor planning and runaway technology have bequeathed us staggering problems that until recently we have hardly seemed to notice. Marshall McLuhan writes: "If the temperature of the bathwater rises only one degree each half-hour, how will the bather know when to scream?" Urban pollution has accumulated just as imperceptibly for years, and only now is the scream being heard.

We now know that our cities have developed their own perverse ecology, each problem feeding another,

JOHN V. LINDSAY *was first elected mayor of New York City in 1965. He had been a member of the House of Representatives since 1959. He is the author of a new book,* The City.

often attracting "solutions" which merely shift the crisis from one area to another. The need now is to think in terms of total environment. No area of city government or industry can act any longer without regard for ecological consequences. Ecology cannot be thought of as a department of government or the job of a few, but as a web of values that permeates all urban thinking.

One point is clear: Technology produced the crisis and technology can end it—if we are thoughtful in using it and willing to pay the price. More expensive but less poisonous fuels are available, and more and more effective filters and gas traps are being developed. Techniques are known whereby garbage can be compressed or burned, with the recycling of potentially valuable waste into chemical by-products and building materials. We know how to package consumer goods in materials that save space and decay rapidly. Effective sewage techniques are old and familiar. All that is needed is the money and the will.

I do not mean that solutions will come quickly or easily, if only because of the enduring political habits of this nation. The cities have been shortchanged by the states and the Federal Government for so long that it would be surprising indeed if the same pattern does not evolve in the current environmental crusade. Already many are using the term "ecology" in its narrowest sense, as if the need to protect our resources is a kind of conservation that stops at city borders.

The city *is* the environment for a growing majority of our citizens. It would be as shortsighted to save the countryside at the expense of the city as it would be to allow ecology to grow into a middle-class whites-only movement. Lead poisoning, rats, the filth of the slums are just as much environmental problems as saving the redwoods and healing the scars of strip mining.

We owe a large debt to those individuals and groups, on campuses and around the country, whose missionary interest in ecology has now burst upon the national consciousness with the fervor of a crusade. But the sudden emergence of this issue may have raised some unreal expectations, the foremost being that ecology is somehow above politics, uniting Northerner and Southerner, Republican and Democrat, left and right. ("After all, no one is pro-pollution.")

After the political exhaustion of 1968, and the heavy drain of our war in Vietnam, the nation badly needs to feel a common sense of mission and unity. But ecology can hardly make our differences disappear. If, for instance, the left is given to believe that it must mute its peace activities for the sake of reclaiming the environment, if ecology is made to seem a cover for our differences rather than a coalition to solve one of them, then the movement is doomed to disillusion.

Where there are priorities there is politics, and the movement to reclaim our environment is no exception. That movement will require billions of dollars over a long haul, and that money will not be available until our expensive commitment in Southeast Asia comes to an end. Even then, extensive politicking will be necessary to sort out priorities of reclamation and to sustain the political pressure necessary for reform. In the cities, overlapping jurisdictions and the current complex relations with suburbs, some of them in adjoining states, assure us cleaning up the environment offers no vacation from politics.

In the cities, the first problem is one of morale. Many studies have indicated a pervasive feeling of hopelessness about the city, a sense that our urban centers are out of control. Littering and slovenly habits that degrade urban life are viewed as simple expressions of this attitude, and the first priority is to change it with concrete reforms, however small at first, that residents can appreciate.

City governments must lead, but the time is long past when solutions to complex problems could be imposed from the top. The aim should be rather to take advantage of the new awareness and encourage the formation of neighborhood or citizen groups which will fight for their own interests. Already in Brooklyn, neigh-borhood groups are organizing to boycott merchants who consistently befoul the sidewalk and streets. If this becomes a pattern, the apparent functional belief in the inevitability of dirty cities may be reversed.

Air and water are the most discussed environmental problems in the city, and in New York we believe we have made important strides in cutting down pollution. But the broadening of the environmental movement in the cities, and the involvement of those who live in them, will depend on new ideas and small programs. The banning of one-way bottles, for instance, may ap-pear to be a small step, but it would eliminate much of the broken glass and daily waste in cities. Plastic garbage bags would eliminate noise, unnecessary steps for sanitation men, and avoid spillage at the truck. Large Sunday newspapers, much of their poundage unread, could be sold in sections, easing the Monday clean-up and saving untold numbers of trees that are now cut down to provide unread pages. Manufacturers of the ubiquitous beer can and the cellophane cig-arette package, as well as many other packagers, may be persuaded to redesign their products.

With the aid of the Reynolds metal company, New York City is developing a program in which communi-ty organizations will return beverage cans for a half-cent per can bounty—a program which we expect to ex-pand over the next five years to the point where twenty-five to fifty per cent of aluminum cans in the city will be reclaimed. Similarly, cities may consider paying a bounty on the abandoned cars which are be-ginning to engulf the urban scene.

Subways lines may be used for off-hour carting of refuse in special cars and many of the new lines can be planned to tie in with stores along the route so the transfer can take place beneath the streets.

Newly designed automobiles—smaller and electric—would save space and cut pollution. While we are waiting, a smaller, slower, low-compression taxicab would be a feasible advance.

New technology can help us cut down on urban noise—e.g., muted jackhammers and air-conditioners, more attention to quieter aircraft and subways. Honking of auto horns and the playing of radios and tape recorders in public can be prohibited.

Over the decades, each environmental disaster has zoomed to lead to another in an unforeseen but related area. But this interdependence works for the good as well. For instance, New York City may derive electric power as well as a new off-shore island or two from a new incinerating unit now being developed in cooperation with the Department of Health, Education and Welfare. This new unit, compact enough to be located in many neighborhoods of the city, thus reducing expensive hauling costs, shreds waste and burns it more efficiently in a fluidized bed furnace. The off-gases are cleaned by an electrostatic precipitator, and the heat can be used to generate about seventeen megawatts of electricity. It also produces an ash that is ideal fill material. We are currently studying the possibility of using it to build an island in the upper bay that might shield the lower Staten Island beaches from the polluted discharge of the Hudson and hasten the reopening of these beaches for swimming.

Another example of double benefit to the environment is Riverbank, a sewage plant New York is building on the bank of the Hudson to clean our share of that river's pollution. The roof of the low thirty-acre plant, built partly on the shore, partly out into the river, will be developed as a park for the nearby community. Additional acreage will extend the park from 125th Street to 155th Street. The plans, drawn up in consultation with community representatives, include an amphitheater, pools, community center, public dock and fishing pier, restaurant and shops, as well as playing fields for several sports.

Our cities are crowded, land is expensive and scarce.

Multiple use of environmental protection facilities is likely to be necessary if the quality of life in our cities is to be improved.

As we go deeper into the problems and integrate the planning of all city agencies in the light of environmental problems, many new options will open up. In New York, for instance, it may well be that forty miles of efficient new subways will do more for our atmosphere than tinkering with the internal combustion engine. It is clear, at least, that the long range effort to protect the environment must include drastic changes in transportation, in housing, and in commercial activity.

We do not yet know whether a major shift in the economy and consumer habits will be necessary to make the cities what they can and should be. The planned obsolescence of goods which we seem to have adopted as a national policy runs counter to the needs of controlling our burgeoning output of refuse.

"Ours is an age," Lewis Mumford writes in *The City in History,* "in which the increasingly automatic processes of production and urban expansion have displaced the human goals they are supposed to serve. Quantitative production has become, for our mass minded contemporaries, the only imperative goal: They value quantification without qualification."

As the emphasis shifts from the quantity of goods to the quality of life, every aspect of the city's life will have to be looked at in a new light. Attitudes toward production, privacy, space, and civic responsibility—to ourselves and succeeding generations—will have to be rethought. We do not yet know where the quest for the quality of life will take us. All we know is that the trip will be long, difficult, and expensive.

Guests, Briefly*

Man is only a recent visitor to the planet earth. Compared to the billions of years that the primordial forces worked in silence in the vast canyons of cosmic space, he has been here only an infinitesimal moment. The prospect that he will pollute his species back to oblivion is a huge tragedy, but perhaps it is only part of a cycle, a ripple in the contour of evolution, part of the pilgrimage of living things that began with cells and plants and only lately has included man.

The philosopher Alfred Whitehead saw the earth as "a second-rate planet revolving around a second-rate sun." Despite this, the earth has been a gracious host for the few moments its most recent visitor—man—has been here. But it has never guaranteed this species a permanent place; and because man is doing what no other species has ever done —quarreling with Nature—it appears that his presence on earth will be nothing more than a brief guest appearance.

COLMAN McCARTHY
The Washington Post
February 18, 1970

* *Used by permission of* The Washington Post.

The Strategy of Ecosystem Development

by EUGENE P. ODUM

The principles of ecological succession bear importantly on the relationships between man and nature. The framework of successional theory needs to be examined as a basis for resolving man's present environmental crisis. Most ideas pertaining to the development of ecological systems are based on descriptive data obtained by observing changes in biotic communities

Eugene P. Odum *is director of the Institute of Ecology, and Alumni Foundation Professor, at the University of Georgia, Athens. An eminent ecologist, biologist, and ornithologist, he is past president of the Ecological Society of America and has won wide recognition in his field.*

From: Science, *Vol. 164, April 18, 1969. (Washington, D.C.: American Association for the Advancement of Science, 1969) pp. 262-270, with deletions. Reprinted by permission of* Science *and the author.*

over long periods, or on highly theoretical assumptions; very few of the generally accepted hypotheses have been tested experimentally. Some of the confusion, vagueness, and lack of experimental work in this area stems from the tendency of ecologists to regard "succession" as a single straightforward idea; in actual fact, it entails an interacting complex of processes, some of which counteract one another.

As viewed here, ecological succession involves the development of ecosystems; it has many parallels in the developmental biology of organisms, and also in the development of human society. The ecosystem, or ecological system, is considered to be a unit of biological organization made up of all of the organisms in a given area (that is, "community") interacting with the physical environment so that a flow of energy leads to characteristic trophic structure and material cycles within the system. It is the purpose of this article to summarize, in the form of a tabular model, components and stages of development at the ecosystem level as a means of emphasizing those aspects of ecological succession that can be accepted on the basis of present knowledge, those that require more study, and those that have special relevance to human ecology.

Definition of Succession

Ecological succession may be defined in terms of the following three parameters.[1] (i) It is an orderly process of community development that is reasonably directional and, therefore, predictable. (ii) It results from modification of the physical environment by the community; that is, succession is community-controlled even though the physical environment determines the pattern, the rate of change, and often sets limits as to how far development can go. (iii) It culminates in a stabilized ecosystem in which maximum biomass (or high information content) and symbiotic function between organisms are maintained per unit of available energy flow. In a word, the "strategy" of succession as a short-term process is basically the same as the "strategy" of long-term evolutionary development of the biosphere—namely, increased control of, or homeostasis with, the physical environment in the sense of achieving maximum protection from its perturbations. As I illustrate below, the strategy of "maximum protection" (that is, trying to achieve maximum support of complex biomass structure) often conflicts with man's goal of "maximum production" (trying to obtain the highest possible yield). Recognition of the ecological basis for this conflict is, I believe, a first step in establishing rational land-use policies.

The earlier descriptive studies of succession on sand dunes, grasslands, forests, marine shores, or other sites, and more recent functional considerations, have led to the basic theory contained in the definition given above. H. T. Odum and Pinkerton,[2] building on Lotka's[3] "law of maximum energy in biological systems," were the first to point out that succession involves a fundamental shift in energy flows as increasing energy is relegated to maintenance. Margalef[4] has recently documented this bioenergetic basis for succession and has extended the concept.

Changes that occur in major structural and functional characteristics of a developing ecosystem are listed in Table 1. Twenty-four attributes of ecological systems are grouped, for convenience of discussion, under six headings. Trends are emphasized by contrasting the situation in early and late development. The degree of absolute change, the rate of change, and the time required to reach a steady state may vary not only with different climatic and physiographic situations but also with different ecosystem attributes in the same physical environment. Where good data are available, rate-of-change curves are usually convex, with changes occurring most rapidly at the beginning, but bimodal or cyclic patterns may also occur.

Table 1. A tabular model of ecological succession: trends to be expected in the development of ecosystems.

Ecosystem attributes	Developmental stages	Mature stages
Community energetics		
1. Gross production/community respiration (**P/R ration**)	Greater or less than 1	Approaches 1
2. Gross production/standing crop biomass (**P/B ratio**)	High	Low
3. Biomass supported/unit energy flow (**B/E ratio**)	Low	High
4. Net community production (yield)	High	Low
5. Food chains	Linear, predominantly grazing	Weblike, predominantly detritus
Community structure		
6. Total organic matter	Small	Large
7. Inorganic nutrients	Extrabiotic	Intrabiotic
8. Species diversity—variety component	Low	High
9. Species diversity—equitability component	Low	High
10. Biochemical diversity	Low	High
11. Stratification and spatial heterogeneity (pattern diversity)	Poorly organized	Well-organized
Life history		
12. Niche specialization	Broad	Narrow
13. Size of organism	Small	Large
14. Life cycles	Short, simple	Long, complex
Nutrient cycling		
15. Mineral cycles	Open	Closed
16. Nutrient exchange rate, between organisms and environment	Rapid	Slow
17. Role of detritus in nutrient regeneration	Unimportant	Important
Selection pressure		
18. Growth form	For rapid growth ("r-selection")	For feedback control ("k-selection")
19. Production	Quantity	Quality
Overall homeostasis		
20. Internal symbiosis	Undeveloped	Developed
21. Nutrient conservation	Poor	Good
22. Stability (resistance to external perturbations)	Poor	Good
23. Entropy	High	Low
24. Information	Low	High

Bioenergetics of Ecosystem Development

Attributes 1 through 5 in Table 1 represent the bioenergetics of the ecosystem. In the early stages of ecological succession, or in "young nature," so to speak, the rate of primary production or total (gross) photosynthesis (P) exceeds the rate of community respiration (R), so that the P/R ratio is greater than 1. In the special case of organic pollution, the P/R ratio is typically less than 1. In both cases, however, the theory is that P/R approaches 1 as succession occurs. In other words, energy fixed tends to be balanced by the energy cost of maintenance (that is, total community respiration) in the mature or "climax" ecosystem. The P/R ratio, therefore, should be an excellent functional index of the relative maturity of the system.

So long as P exceeds R, organic matter and biomass (B) will accumulate in the system (Table 1, item 6), with the result that ratio P/B will tend to decrease or, conversely, the B/P, B/R, or B/E ratios (where $E=P+R$) will increase (Table 1, items 2 and 3). Theoretically, then, the amount of standing-crop biomass supported by the available energy flow (E) increases to a maximum in the mature or climax stages (Table 1, item 3). As a consequence, the net community production, or yield, in an annual cycle is large in young nature and small or zero in mature nature (Table 1, item 4). . . .

Food Chains and Food Webs

As the ecosystem develops, subtle changes in the network pattern of food chains may be expected. The manner in which organisms are linked together through food tends to be relatively simple and linear in the very early stages of succession, as a consequence of low diversity. Furthermore, heterotrophic utilization of net production occurs predominantly by way of grazing food chains—that is, plant-herbivore-carnivore sequences. In contrast, food chains become complex webs in mature stages, with the bulk of biological energy flow following detritus pathways (Table 1, item 5). In a mature forest, for example, less than 10 percent of annual net production is consumed (that is, grazed) in the living state;[5] most is utilized as dead matter (detritus) through delayed and complex pathways involving as yet little understood animal-microorganism interactions. The time involved in an uninterrupted succession allows for increasingly intimate associations and reciprocal adaptations between plants and animals, which lead to the development of many mechanisms that reduce grazing—such as the development of indigestible supporting tissues (cellulose, lignin, and so on), feedback control between plants and herbivores,[6] and increasing predatory pressure on herbivores.[7] Such mechanisms enable the biological community to maintain the large and complex organic structure that mitigates perturbations of the physical environment. Severe stress or rapid changes brought about by outside forces can, of course, rob the system of these protective mechanisms and allow irruptive, cancerous growths of certain species to occur, as man too often finds to his sorrow. . . .

Diversity and Succession

Perhaps the most controversial of the successional trends pertain to the complex and much discussed subject of diversity.[8] It is important to distinguish between different kinds of diversity indices, since they may not follow parallel trends in the same gradient or developmental series. Four components of diversity are listed in Table 1, items 8 through 11.

The variety of species, expressed as a species-number ratio or a species-area ratio, tends to increase during the early stages of community development. A second component of species diversity is what has been called equitability or evenness,[9] in the apportionment of individuals among the species. For example, two systems each containing 10 species and 100 individuals have the same diversity in terms of species-number ratio but could have widely different equitabilities depending on the apportionment of the 100 individuals among the 10 species—for example, 91-1-1-1-1-1-1-1-1-1 at one extreme or 10 individuals per species at the other. . . .

While an increase in the variety of species together with reduced dominance by any one species or small group of species (that is, increased evenness) can be accepted as a general probability during succession,[10] there are other community changes that may work against these trends. An increase in the size of organisms, an increase in the length and complexity of life histories, and an increase in interspecific competition that may result in competitive exclusion of species (Table 1, items 12-14) are trends that may reduce the number of species that can live in a given area. In the bloom stage of succession organisms tend to be small and to have simple life histories and rapid rates of reproduction. Changes in size appear to be a consequence of, or an adaptation to, a shift in nutrients from inorganic to organic (Table 1, item 7). In a mineral nutrient-rich environment, small size is of selective advantage, especially to autotrophs, because of the greater surface-to-volume ratio. As the ecosystem develops, however, inorganic nutrients tend to become more and more tied up in the biomass (that is, to become intrabiotic), so that the selective advantage shifts to larger organisms (either larger individuals of the same species or larger species, or both) which have greater storage capacities and more complex life histories, thus are adapted to exploiting seasonal or periodic releases of nutrients or other resources. The question of whether the seemingly direct relationship between organism size and stability is the result of positive feedback or is merely fortuitous remains unanswered.[11]

Thus, whether or not species diversity continues to increase during succession will depend on whether the

increase in potential niches resulting from increased biomass, stratification (Table 1, item 9), and other consequences of biological organization exceeds the coun-
tereffects of increasing size and competition. No one
has yet been able to catalogue all the species in any
sizable area, much less follow total species diversity in
a successional series. Data are so far available only for
segments of the community (trees, birds, and so on).
Margalef postulates that diversity will tend to peak during the early or middle stages of succession and then
decline in the climax. In a study of bird populations
along a successional gradient we found a bimodal pattern;[12] the number of species increased during the
early stages of old-field succession, declined during the
early forest stages, and then increased again in the mature forest.

Species variety, equitability, and stratification are
only three aspects of diversity which change during succession. Perhaps an even more important trend is an
increase in the diversity of organic compounds, not only
of those within the biomass but also of those excreted
and secreted into the media (air, soil, water) as by-products of the increasing community metabolism. An increase in such "biochemical diversity" (Table 1, item
10) is illustrated by the increase in the variety of plant
pigments along a successional gradient in aquatic situations, as described by Margalef. [13] Biochemical diversity within populations, or within systems as a whole,
has not yet been systematically studied to the degree
the subject of species diversity has been. Consequently,
few generalizations can be made, except that it seems
safe to say that, as succession progresses, organic extra-
metabolites probably serve increasingly important functions as regulators which stabilize the growth and composition of the ecosystem. Such metabolites may, in
fact, be extremely important in preventing populations
from overshooting the equilibrial density, thus in reducing oscillations as the system develops stability.

The cause-and-effect relationship between diversity

and stability is not clear and needs to be investigated from many angles. If it can be shown that biotic diversity does indeed enhance physical stability in the ecosystem, or is the result of it, then we would have an important guide for conservation practice. Preservation of hedgerows, woodlots, noneconomic species, noneutrophicated waters, and other biotic variety in man's landscape could then be justified on scientific as well as esthetic grounds, even though such preservation often must result in some reduction in the production of food or other immediate consumer needs. In other words, is variety only the spice of life, or is it a necessity for the long life of the total ecosystem comprising man and nature?

Nutrient Cycling

An important trend in successional development is the closing or "tightening" of the biogeochemical cycling of major nutrients, such as nitrogen, phosphorus, and calcium (Table 1, items 15-17). Mature systems, as compared to developing ones, have a greater capacity to entrap and hold nutrients for cycling within the system. For example, Bormann and Likens [14] have estimated that only 8 kilograms per hectare out of a total pool of exchangeable calcium of 365 kilograms per hectare is lost per year in stream outflow from a North Temperate watershed covered with a mature forest. Of this, about 3 kilograms per hectare is replaced by rainfall, leaving only 5 kilograms to be obtained from weathering of the underlying rocks in order for the system to maintain mineral balance. Reducing the volume of the vegetation, or otherwise setting the succession back to a younger state, results in increased water yield by way of stream outflow, [15] but this greater outflow is accompanied by greater losses of nutrients, which may also produce downstream eutrophication. Unless there is a compensating increase in the rate of weathering, the exchangeable pool of nutrients suffers gradual depletion (not to mention possible effects on soil structure resulting from erosion). High fertility in "young systems" which have open nutrient cycles cannot be maintained without compensating inputs of new nutrients; examples of such practice are the continuous-flow culture of algae, or intensive agriculture where large amounts of fertilizer are imported into the system each year.

Because rates of leaching increase in a latitudinal gradient from the poles to the equator, the role of the biotic community in nutrient retention is especially important in the high-rainfall areas of the subtropical and tropical latitudes, including not only land areas but also estuaries. Theoretically, as one goes equatorward, a larger percentage of the available nutrient pool is tied up in the biomass and a correspondingly lower percentage is in the soil or sediment. This theory, however, needs testing, since data to show such a geographical trend are incomplete. It is perhaps significant that conventional North Temperate row-type agriculture, which represents a very youthful type of ecosystem, is successful in the humid tropics only if carried out in a system of "shifting agriculture" in which the crops alternate with periods of natural vegetative redevelopment. Tree culture and the semiaquatic culture of rice provide much better nutrient retention and consequently have a longer life expectancy on a given site in these warmer latitudes.

Selection Pressure: Quantity versus Quality

MacArthur and Wilson[16] have reviewed stages of colonization of islands which provide direct parallels with stages in ecological succession on continents. Species with high rates of reproduction and growth, they find, are more likely to survive in the early uncrowded stages of island colonization. In contrast, selection pressure favors species with lower growth potential but better capabilities for competitive survival under the equilibrium density of late stages. Using the terminology of growth equations, where r is the intrinsic rate of increase and K is the upper asymptote or equilibrium population size, we may say that "r selection" predominates in early colonization, with "K selection" prevailing as more and more species and individuals attempt to colonize (Table 1, item 18). The same sort of thing is even seen within the species in certain "cyclic" northern insects in which "active" genetic strains found at low densities are replaced at high densities by "sluggish" strains that are adapted to crowding.[17]

Genetic changes involving the whole biota may be presumed to accompany the successional gradient, since, as described above, quantity production characterizes the young ecosystem while quality production and feedback control are the trademarks of the mature system (Table 1, item 19). Selection at the ecosystem level may be primarily interspecific, since species replacement is a characteristic of successional series or seres. However, in most well-studied seres there seem to be a few early successional species that are able to persist through to late stages. Whether genetic changes contribute to adaptation in such species has not been determined, so far as I know, but studies on population genetics of *Drosophila* suggest that changes in genetic composition could be important in population regulation.[18] Certainly, the human population, if it survives beyond its present rapid growth stage, is destined to be more and more affected by such selection pressures as adaptation to crowding becomes essential.

Overall Homeostasis

This brief review of ecosystem development emphasizes the complex nature of processes that interact.

While one may well question whether all the trends described are characteristic of all types of ecosystems, there can be little doubt that the net result of community actions is symbiosis, nutrient conservation, stability, a decrease in entropy, and an increase in information (Table 1, items 20-24). The overall strategy is, as I stated at the beginning of this article, directed toward achieving as large and diverse an organic structure as is possible within the limits set by the available energy input and the prevailing physical conditions of existence (soil, water, climate, and so on). As studies of biotic communities become more functional and sophisticated, one is impressed with the importance of mutualism, parasitism, predation, commensalism, and other forms of symbiosis. Partnership between unrelated species is often noteworthy (for example, that between coral coelenterates and algae, or between mycorrhizae and trees). In many cases, at least, biotic control of grazing, population density, and nutrient cycling provide the chief positive-feedback mechanisms that contribute to stability in the mature system by preventing overshoots and destructive oscillations. The intriguing question is, Do mature ecosystems age, as organisms do? In other words, after a long period of relative stability or "adulthood," do ecosystems again develop unbalanced metabolism and become more vulnerable to diseases and other perturbations?

Relevance of Ecosystem Development Theory to Human Ecology

Figure 1 depicts a basic conflict between the strategies of man and of nature. The "bloom-type" relationships, as exhibited by the 30-day microcosm or the 30-year forest, illustrate man's present idea of how nature should be directed. For example, the goal of agriculture or intensive forestry, as now generally practiced, is to achieve high rates of production of readily harvestable

uses. Many essential life-cycle resources, not to mention recreational and esthetic needs, are best provided man by the less "productive" landscapes. In other words, the landscape is not just a supply depot but is also the *oikos*—the home—in which we must live. Until recently mankind has more or less taken for granted the gas-exchange, water-purification, nutrient-cycling, and other protective functions of self-maintaining ecosystems, chiefly because neither his numbers nor his environmental manipulations have been great enough to affect regional and global balances. Now, of course, it is painfully evident that such balances are being affected, often detrimentally. The "one problem, one solution approach" is no longer adequate and must be replaced by some form of ecosystem analysis that considers man as a part of, not apart from, the environment. .

The most pleasant and certainly the safest landscape to live in is one containing a variety of crops, forests, lakes, streams, roadsides, marshes, seashores, and "waste places"—in other words, a mixture of communities of different ecological ages. As individuals we more or less instinctively surround our houses with protective, nonedible cover (trees, shrubs, grass) at the same time that we strive to coax extra bushels from our cornfield. We all consider the cornfield a "good thing," of course, but most of us would not want to live there, and it would certainly be suicidal to cover the whole land area of the biosphere with cornfields, since the boom and bust oscillation in such a situation would be severe.

The basic problem facing organized society today boils down to determining in some objective manner when we are getting "too much of a good thing." This is a completely new challenge to mankind because, up until now, he has had to be concerned largely with too little rather than too much. Thus, concrete is a "good thing," but not if half the world is covered with it. Insecticides are "good things," but not when used, as they now are, in an indiscriminate and wholesale manner. Likewise, water impoundments have proved to be very useful man-made additions to the landscape, but obviously we don't want the whole country inundated. Vast man-made lakes solve some problems, at least temporarily, but yield comparative little food or fiber, and, because of high evaporative losses, they may not even be the best device for storing water; it might better be stored in the watershed, or underground in aquafers. Also, the cost of building large dams is a drain on already overtaxed revenues. Although as individuals we readily recognize that we can have too many dams or other large-scale environmental changes, governments are so fragmented and lacking in systems-analysis capabilities that there is no effective mechanism whereby negative feedback signals can be received and acted on before there has been a serious overshoot. Thus, today there are governmental agencies, spurred on by popular and political enthusiasm for dams, that are putting on the drawing boards plans for damming every river and stream in North America!

Society needs, and must find as quickly as possible, a way to deal with the landscape as a whole, so that manipulative skills (that is, technology) will not run too far ahead of our understanding of the impact of change. Recently a national ecological center outside of government and a coalition of governmental agencies have been proposed as two possible steps in the establishment of a political control mechanism for dealing with major environmental questions. The soil conservation movement in America is an excellent example of a program dedicated to the consideration of the whole farm or the whole watershed as an ecological unit. Soil conservation is well understood and supported by the public. However, soil conservation organizations have remained too exclusively farm-oriented, and have not yet risen to the challenge of the urban-rural landscape, where lie today's most serious problems. We do, then, have potential mechanisms in American society that could speak for the ecosystem as a whole, but none of them are really operational. . . .[19]

Pulse Stability

A more or less regular but acute physical perturbation imposed from without can maintain an ecosystem at some intermediate point in the developmental sequence, resulting in, so to speak, a compromise between youth and maturity. What I would term "fluctuating water level ecosystems" are good examples. Estuaries, and intertidal zones in general, are maintained in an early, relatively fertile stage by the tides, which provide the energy for rapid nutrient cycling. Likewise, fresh-water marshes, such as the Florida Everglades, are held at an early successional stage by the seasonal fluctuations in water levels. The dry-season drawdown speeds up aerobic decomposition of accumulated organic matter, releasing nutrients that, on reflooding, support a wet-season bloom in productivity. The life histories of many organisms are intimately coupled to this periodicity. The wood stork, for example, breeds when the water levels are falling and the small fish on which it feeds become concentrated and easy to catch in the drying pools. If the water level remains high during the usual dry season or fails to rise in the wet season, the stork will not nest.[20] Stabilizing water levels in the Everglades by means of dikes, locks, and impoundments, as is now advocated by some, would, in my opinion, destroy rather than preserve the Everglades as we now know them just as surely as complete drainage would. Without periodic drawdowns and fires, the shallow basins would fill up with organic matter and succession would proceed from the present pond-and-prairie condition toward a scrub or swamp forest.

It is strange that man does not readily recognize the importance of recurrent changes in water level in a natural situation such as the Everglades when similar pulses are the basis for some of his most enduring food culture systems.[21] Alternate filling and draining of ponds has been a standard procedure in fish culture for centuries in Europe and the Orient. The flooding, draining, and soil-aeration procedure in rice culture is another example. The rice paddy is thus the cultivated analogue of the natural marsh or the intertidal ecosystem.

Fire is another physical factor whose periodicity has been of vital importance to man and nature over the centuries. Whole biotas, such as those of the African grasslands and the California chaparral, have become adapted to periodic fires producing what ecologists often call "fire climaxes."[22] Man uses fire deliberately to maintain such climaxes or to set back succession to some desired point. In the southeastern coastal plain, for example, light fires of moderate frequency can maintain a pine forest against the encroachment of older successional stages which, at the present time at least, are considered economically less desirable. The fire-controlled forest yields less wood than a tree farm does (that is, young trees, all of about the same age, planted in rows and harvested on a short rotation schedule), but it provides a greater protective cover for the landscape, wood of higher quality, and a home for game birds (quail, wild turkey, and so on) which could not survive in a tree farm. The fire climax, then, is an example of a compromise between production simplicity and protection diversity.

It should be emphasized that pulse stability works only if there is a complete community (including not only plants but animals and microorganisms) adapted to the particular intensity and frequency of the perturbation. Adaptation—operation of the selection process —requires times measurable on the evolutionary scale. Most physical stresses introduced by man are too sudden, too violent, or too arrhythmic for adaptation to occur at the ecosystem level, so severe oscillation rather than stability results. In many cases, at least, modification of naturally adapted ecosystems for cultural purposes would seem preferable to complete redesign.

Prospects for a Detritus Agriculture

As indicated above, heterotrophic utilization of primary production in mature ecosystems involves largely a delayed consumption of detritus. There is no reason why man cannot make greater use of detritus and thus obtain food or other products from the more protective type of ecosystem. Again, this would represent a compromise, since the short-term yield could not be as great as the yield obtained by direct exploitation of the grazing food chain. A detritus agriculture, however, would have some compensating advantages. Present agricultural strategy is based on selection for rapid growth and edibility in food plants, which, of course, make them vulnerable to attack by insects and disease. Consequently, the more we select for succulence and growth, the more effort we must invest in the chemical control of pests; this effort, in turn, increases the likelihood of our poisoning useful organisms, not to mention ourselves. Why not also practice the reverse strategy—that is, select plants which are essentially unpalatable, or which produce their own systemic insecticides while they are growing, and then convert the net production into edible products by microbial and chemical enrichment in food factories? We could then devote our biochemical genius to the enrichment process instead of fouling up our living space with chemical poisons. . . .

By tapping the detritus food chain man can also obtain an appreciable harvest from many natural systems without greatly modifying them or destroying their protective and esthetic value. Oyster culture and other mariculture in natural waters are good examples of using natural productivity. . . .

The Compartment Model

Successful though they often are, compromise systems

are not suitable nor desirable for the whole landscape. More emphasis needs to be placed on compartmentalization, so that growth-type, steady-state, and intermediate-type ecosystems can be linked with urban and industrial areas for mutual benefit. Knowing the transfer coefficients that define the flow of energy and the movement of materials and organisms (including man) between compartments, it should be possible to determine, through analog-computer manipulation, rational limits for the size and capacity of each compartment. We might start, for example, with a simplified model, shown in Fig. 2, consisting of four compartments of equal area, partitioned according to the basic biotic-function criterion—that is, according to whether the area is (i) productive, (ii) protective, (iii) a compromise between (i) and (ii) or (iv), urban-industrial. By continually refining the transfer coefficients on the basis of real world situations, and by increasing and decreasing the size and capacity of each compartment through computer simulation, it would be possible to determine objectively the limits that must eventually be imposed on each compartment in order to maintain regional and global balances in the exchange of vital energy and of materials. A systems-analysis procedure provides at least one approach to the solution of the basic dilemma posed by the question "How do we determine when we are getting too much of a good thing?" Also it provides a means of evaluating the energy drains imposed on ecosystems by pollution, radiation, harvest, and other stresses.[23]

Implementing any kind of compartmentalization plan, of course, would require procedures for zoning the landscape and restricting the use of some land and water areas. While the principle of zoning in cities is universally accepted, the procedures now followed do not work very well because zoning restrictions are too easily overturned by short-term economic and population pressures. Zoning the landscape would require a whole new order of thinking. Greater use of legal measures pro-

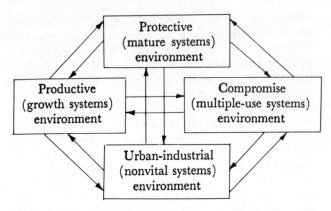

Fig. 2. Compartment model of the basic kinds of environment required by man, partitioned according to ecosystem development and life-cycle resource criteria.

viding for tax relief, restrictions on use, scenic ease-ments, and public ownership will be required if appre-ciable land and water areas are to be held in the "pro-tective" categories. Several states (for example, New Jersey and California), where pollution and population pressure are beginning to hurt, have made a start in this direction by enacting "open space" legislation de-signed to get as much unoccupied land as possible into a "protective" status so that future uses can be planned on a rational and scientific basis. The United States as a whole is fortunate in that large areas of the coun-try are in national forests, parks, wildlife refuges, and so on. The fact that such areas, as well as the border-ing oceans, are not quickly exploitable gives us time for the accelerated ecological study and programming needed to determine what proportions of different types of landscape provide a safe balance between man and nature. The open oceans, for example, should for-ever be allowed to remain protective rather than pro-ductive territory, if Alfred Redfield's[24] assumptions are correct. Redfield views the oceans, the major part of the hydrosphere, as the biosphere's governor, which slows down and controls the rate of decomposition and nutrient regeneration, thereby creating and maintaining the highly aerobic terrestrial environment to which the higher forms of life, such as man, are adapted. Eutrophication of the ocean in a last-ditch effort to feed the populations of the land could well have an adverse effect on the oxygen reservoir in the atmosphere.

Until we can determine more precisely how far we may safely go in expanding intensive agriculture and urban sprawl at the expense of the protective landscape, it will be good insurance to hold inviolate as much of the latter as possible. Thus, the preservation of natural areas is not a peripheral luxury for society but a capital investment from which we expect to draw interest. Also, it may well be that restrictions in the use of land and water are our only practical means of avoiding overpopulation or too great an exploitation of resources, or both. Interestingly enough, restriction of land use is the analogue of a natural behavioral control mechanism known as "territoriality" by which many species of animals avoid crowding and social stress.[25]

Since the legal and economic problems pertaining to zoning and compartmentalization are likely to be thorny, I urge law schools to establish departments, or institutes, of "landscape law" and to start training "landscape lawyers" who will be capable not only of clarifying existing procedures but also of drawing up new enabling legislation for consideration by state and national governing bodies. At present, society is concerned —and rightly so—with human rights, but environmental rights are equally vital. The "one man one vote" idea is important, but so also is a "one man one hectare" proposition.

Education, as always, must play a role in increasing man's awareness of his dependence on the natural environment. Perhaps we need to start teaching the principles of ecosystem in the third grade. A grammar school primer on man and his environment could logically consist of four chapters, one for each of the four essential kinds of environment, shown diagrammatically in Fig. 2.

Of the many books and articles that are being written these days about man's environmental crisis, I would like to cite two that go beyond "crying out in alarm" to suggestions for bringing about a reorientation of the goals of society. Garrett Hardin, in a recent article in *Science,*[26] points out that, since the optimum population density is less than the maximum, there is no strictly technical solution to the problem of pollution caused by overpopulation; a solution, he suggests, can only be achieved through moral and legal means of "mutual coercion, mutually agreed upon by the majority of people." Earl F. Murphy, in his book entitled *Governing Nature,*[27] emphasizes that the regulatory approach alone is not enough to protect life-cycle resources, such as air and water, that cannot be allowed to deteriorate. He discusses permit systems, effluent charges, receptor levies, assessment, and cost-internalizing procedures as economic incentives for achieving Hardin's "mutually agreed upon coercion."

It goes without saying that the tabular model for ecosystem development which I have presented here has many parallels in the development of human society itself. In the pioneer society, as in the pioneer ecosystem, high birth rates, rapid growth, high economic profits, and exploitation of accessible and unused resources are advantageous, but, as the saturation level is approached, these drives must be shifted to considerations of symbiosis (that is,"civil rights," "law and order," "education," and "culture"), birth control, and the recycling of resources. A balance between youth and maturity in the socio-environmental system is, therefore, the really basic goal that must be achieved if man as a species is to successfully pass through the present rapid-growth stage, to which he is clearly well adapted, to the ultimate equilibrium-density stage, of which he as yet shows little understanding and to which he now shows little tendency to adapt.

References and Notes

1. E. P. Odum, *Ecology* (Holt, Rinehart & Winston, New York, 1963), chap. 6.
2. H. T. Odum and R. C. Pinkerton, *Amer. Scientist* **43,** 331 (1955).
3. A. J. Lotka, *Elements of Physical Biology* (Williams and Wilkins, Baltimore, 1925).
4. R. Margalef, *Advan. Frontiers Plant Sci.* **2,** 137 (1963); *Amer. Naturalist* **97,** 357 (1963).
5. J. R. Bray, *Oikos* **12,** 70 (1961).
6. D. Pimentel, *Amer. Naturalist* **95,** 65 (1961).
7. R. T. Paine, *ibid.* **100,** 65 (1966).
8. For selected general discussions of patterns of species diversity, see E. H. Simpson, *Nature* **163,** 688 (1949); C. B. Williams, *J. Animal Ecol.* **22,** 14 (1953); G. E. Hutchinson, *Amer. Naturalist* **93,** 145 (1959); R. Margalef, *Gen. Systems* **3,** 36 (1958); R. MacArthur and J. MacArthur, *Ecology* **42,** 594 (1961); N. G. Hairston, *ibid.* **40,** 404 (1959); B. C. Patten, *J. Marine Res. (Sears Found. Marine Res.)* **20,** 57 (1960); E. G. Leigh, *Proc. Nat. Acad. Sci. U.S.* **55,** 777 (1965); E. R. Pianka, *Amer. Naturalist* **100,** 33 (1966); E. C. Pielou, *J. Theoret. Biol.* **10,** 370 (1966).
9. M. Lloyd and R. J. Ghelardi, *J. Animal Ecol.* **33,** 217 (1964); E. C. Pielou, *J. Theoret. Biol.* **13,** 131 (1966).
10. In our studies of natural succession following grain culture, both the species-to-numbers and the equitability indices increased for all trophic levels but especially for predators and parasites. Only 44 percent of the species in the natural ecosystem were phytophagous, as compared to 77 percent in the grain field.
11. J. T. Bonner, *Size and Cycle* (Princeton Univ. Press, Princeton, N.J., 1963); P. Frank, *Ecology* **49,** 355 (1968).
12. D. W. Johnston and E. P. Odum, *Ecology* **37,** 50 (1956).
13. R. Margalef, *Oceanog. Marine Biol. Annu. Rev.* **5,** 257 (1967).
14. F. H. Bormann and G. E. Likens, *Science* **155,** 424 (1967).
15. Increased water yield following reduction of vegetative cover has been frequently demonstrated in experimental watersheds throughout the world [see A. R. Hibbert, in *International Symposium on Forest Hydrology* (Pergamon Press, New York, 1967), pp. 527-543]. Data on the long-term hydrologic budget (rainfall input relative to stream outflow) are available at many of these sites, but mineral budgets have yet to be systematically studied. Again, this is a prime objective in the "ecosystem analysis" phase of the International Biological Program.

16. R. H. MacArthur and E. O. Wilson, *Theory of Island Bio-geography* (Princeton Univ. Press, Princeton, N.J., 1967).
17. Examples are the tent caterpillar [see W. G. Wellington, *Can. J. Zool.* **35**, 293 (1957)] and the larch budworm [see W. Baltensweiler, *Can. Entomologist* **96**, 792 (1964)].
18. F. J. Ayala, *Science* **162**, 1453 (1968).
19. Ira Rubinoff in discussing the proposed sea-level canal joining the Atlantic and Pacific oceans [*Science* **161**, 857 (1968)], calls for a "control commission for environmental manipulation" with "broad powers of approving, disapproving, or modifying all major alterations of the marine or terrestrial environments. . . ."
20. See M. P. Kahl, *Ecol. Monographs* **34**, 97 (1964).
21. The late Aldo Leopold remarked long ago [*Symposium on Hydrobiology* (Univ. of Wisconsin Press, Madison, 1941), p. 17] that man does not perceive organic behavior in systems unless he has built them himself. Let us hope it will not be necessary to rebuild the entire biosphere before we recognize the worth of natural systems!
22. See C. F. Cooper, *Sci. Amer.* **204**, 150 (April 1961).
23. See H. T. Odum, in *Symposium on Primary Productivity and Mineral Cycling in Natural Ecosystems*, H. E. Young, Ed. (Univ. of Maine Press, Orono, 1967), p. 81; ———, in *Pollution and Marine Ecology* (Wiley, New York, 1967), p. 99; K. E. F. Watt, *Ecology and Resource Management* (McGraw-Hill, New York, 1968).
24. A. C. Redfield, *Amer. Scientist* **46**, 205 (1958).
25. R. Ardrey, *The Territorial Imperative* (Atheneum, New York, 1967).
26. G. Hardin, *Science* **162**, 1243 (1968).
27. E. F. Murphy, *Governing Nature* (Quadrangle Books, Chicago, 1967).

. . . Man is a unique *animal*. He is the result of over a 100 million years of evolution as a mammal, of over 45 million years as a primate, of over 15 million years as an ape. His human uniqueness is, at most, 2 million years old or less. The refined human neurological and physical attributes are but a few hundred thousand years old. Knowing what we do concerning evolutionary rates, we must conclude that modern man has experienced but relatively few major genetic innovations. Thus our major chemical-physiological patterns, those basic, inner, seething, and mysterious chemical frameworks of the human animal, be they digestion, nervous system, or sex, are much more similar to those of our primate relatives than they are different. They, as well as we, are nothing more or less than the result of natural selection in nature. As unique as we may think we are, we are nevertheless programmed genetically to need clear air and sunshine, a green landscape and unpolluted water, and natural animal and vegetable foods. To be healthy, which after all has nothing to do with IQ or culture, means simply allowing our bodies to react in the way that 100 millions of years of evolution in tropical or subtropical nature have equipped us to do. . . .

Thus the endless arguments as to what kind of environment man needs (short of daily intake of appropriate calories and vitamins) are unnecessary, because the answer is obvious: *The optimum human environment is one in which the human animal can have maximum contact with the natural (evolutionary) environment in which he evolved* and for which all our basic processes are genetically programmed, yet *in which at the same time the many advantages of civilization are not sacrificed*. It is a compromise—this humane human environment—between our genetic heritage, which we cannot deny except at great emotional and physical misery, and the fruits of an unbelievably varied civilization which we are loath to give up.

If the concrete and steel city, this great arena of

bright lights and stimulation as well as of heartbreak, the largest, filthiest, most seductive, and most dangerous living thing in the world, turns man into an asocial, erratic, and sick animal; if urbanization degrades human society through increased emotional stress, crime, delinquency, slums, and other neuroses and psychoses, it is because the genetic flexibility of the human animal trapped in this necropolis is not great enough, because no natural selection has given us gene combinations to cope with this environment, and no natural selection ever will. Our human genetic adaptations are here simply out of evolutionary context. Man is dehumanized in the city because of his near total victory over nature. When the last tree dies in Brooklyn, dehumanization will spread like a plague. We may look upon megalopolis as a giant experiment in sensory deprivation. And, eventually, total destruction of nature will bring total destruction of man. . . .

Studies have shown that a person bored with monotony will show continuously highly vacillating alpha brain waves that keep his body on alert (this again, no doubt, evolutionarily selected). In a person whose mind or body is active, due to diversity of physical activity or mental processes, the brain waves will flatten out to beta-waves, which let his system relax more. Who knows what the monotony of asphalt jungles, or of cornfields, does to the nervous system of a man? And who cares to study it? Biotic and cultural diversity, from the neurological standpoint, then, may well be an important attribute to general health, a psychiatric safety valve that is not a luxury but an indispensable human need.

Support for the therapeutic effects of nature comes not only from the commonplace negative association of ill health with cities and slums and from the positive fact that we go vacationing in the natural diversity of mountain, seashore, or forest, but also from the therapeutic effects of the out-of-doors on the mentally ill. The interesting and encouraging results of M. Weis-

mann et al. (1965) of Maryland in taking the chronical-
ly hospitalized (for 2 to 30 years) mentally ill out camping are worth noting. Here, hiking through the woods
was, next to eating, the most cherished activity, and
nearly 40 percent of the 90 patients were released into
their communities within 30 months—this as a result of
only a 2 weeks' camping experience. Other studies
have shown similar results. Many factors may well be
involved here; but, could one not suppose that, in a
person whose cultural load has twisted his normal functioning into bizarre reactions, his most basic inner
drives will be functioning like a psychological gyrostat
especially well in the environment where they originally evolved millions of years ago? Leaves and trees do
not talk back; they are a non-aggressive, neutral element, free of danger; and, especially important, they
do not represent intraspecific competition. They rest
the overstrained reaction system of the sick man to the
point where he can, so to speak, pick up the pieces of
his later-acquired evolutionary or social adaptations and
begin to function in more complex spheres. . . .

We must farm, but must we do it often so blindly?
Must we destroy this diversity without heed to other
values, including often direct agricultural ones? By
pesticides and other means we are exterminating countless species of plants and animals and whole plant associations (such as the American Prairie) with a ferocity
that only the human species is capable of, tens of thousands of species whose roles in the ecology of land we
cannot even guess at, whose uses to man we do not
even know, and will not know for many, many years to
come. And, as David Gates recently said, we are depriv-
ing future generations of a chance to *ever* properly
study or understand the living communities, the ecosystems, of the earth. Once extinct, a species or a community is gone forever. . . .

The sterility of eagles and depletion of other birds,
the tremendous fish kills in our rivers, and the disap-
pearance of countless insects are but some of the un-

foreseen side-effects of pesticides. Much more than half of the 250 species of Colombian parrots have become extinct during the past decades as a result of habitat destruction and pesticides, according to Roger Tory Peterson. Can we afford to continue to use these chemicals? Nevertheless, the entomologists talk about risk-benefit evaluations and the Ribicoff committee "found no reliable evidence to suggest that the benefit-risk equation was *presently* unbalanced in any *significant* ways, (but) much more information is needed. . . ."

It has been recently shown that most pesticides are *mutagenic* in plant tissue and very probably in animal tissue as well. Human fat tissue may contain from 2 to 30 ppm of DDT. The consequences of this are unknown. Thus pesticides are an example of the application of dangerous knowledge (in the sense of Van Potter), i.e., knowledge applied before we know the consequences of the application—a blind application. . . .

The far-reaching and irrevocable destructive effects of technology on nature have to be seen to be believed, especially in the fragile tropics; thus it will not do to stop the fearless "winnowing and sifting" of the truth at our universities and colleges. To encourage hundreds of students to regard Rachel Carson's *Silent Spring* with a smirk without being required to read it (or even inducing them not to read it), or to continue to preach cornucopic doctrines of superabundance and technological solutions to hunger, is to make students instruments of a carefully perpetuated ignorance, because, when selected knowledge is regarded as sin, ignorance must be transmitted in its stead. This will not do. We must reshape our agricultural horizons to ecological facts of life. The responsibilities are awful. For this is the only biosphere that is fit for man.

the auto and the air

Why
the Birds Cough

by WILLIAM STEIF

ON THE hot, muggy evening of August 28 last year, 30,000 people, mostly young, crowded onto the Boston Common, the big center city park, to hear a rock group named the Chamber Brothers. Many came in automobiles, which they parked beneath the Common in a three-tier, 1,500-car municipal garage built a few years ago.

In all, 1,300 cars were in the garage when the show was over. Much of the audience descended into the garage and, almost simultaneously, drivers turned on their motors and headed for the three toll-booth exits.

Within minutes youngsters began staggering out of the garage on foot, gasping and choking. Others passed out in their cars. Police carried at least twenty unconscious persons out of the garage. Ambulances took twenty-five persons to two hospitals, while oxygen was given to many other young people on the grounds of

WILLIAM STEIF *is a Washington staff writer for the Scripps-Howard News Alliance who specializes in coverage of environmental problems.*

the Common. Fortunately, a quick-witted city official saw what was happening and ordered the toll-takers to stop taking tolls so that the garage could be cleared swiftly. Everyone recovered soon and went home. Twenty-four hours later the incident was nearly forgotten.

Yet the near-disaster at the Boston Common is an index to how air pollution from the auto has created a crisis in the nation.

There are other indices, some almost unnoticed.

Los Angeles—"where the birds cough"—is notorious for its auto-produced smog. Indeed, wealthy Angelenos used to drive down to Palm Springs, a desert resort 110 miles away, to escape the Los Angeles smog. But last summer, for the first time, long fingers of tear-producing, yellow-gray smog appeared over Palm Springs.

Or consider the experience of the twenty-two men working the toll booths at either end of the Brooklyn Battery Tunnel—all but one in their twenties and thirties. More than half were found to have dizzy spells from a higher-than-average concentration of carbon monoxide in their lungs. Over the one-month period in which the twenty-two were studied, five of the men had blackouts.

The death rate from bronchitis and emphysema in the United States today is nine times as high as it was twenty years ago. At the present rate of increase, 180,000 Americans will die of these lung ailments in 1983.

The extent to which the nation's automobiles can be blamed for its polluted air has been known for years, but only in recent months have American political leaders, from President Nixon on down, been willing to listen to their scientific advisers and point the finger directly at the manufacturers in Detroit. In his State of the Union message at the end of January, the President said: "The automobile is our worst polluter of the air. Adequate control requires further advances in engine design and fuel composition. We shall intensify our research, set increasingly strict standards, and strengthen enforcement procedures—and we shall do it now."

Senator Edmund S. Muskie, Maine Democrat, welcomed this "rhetoric of concern" and promptly offered a detailed $975 million air pollution program which he hoped Mr. Nixon would support. Another leading environmentalist, Senator Gaylord Nelson, Wisconsin Democrat, went even further and suggested that the auto's internal combustion engine should be phased out starting this year unless the auto manufacturers develop pollution-free exhausts. The Democratic leadership in both House and Senate challenged the President to increase funding greatly for clean air programs.

In California, which pioneered in smog control legislation, and in some other states, politicians are vying with one another to produce tougher proposals aimed at the internal combustion engine. And in mid-February, as part of a thirty-seven-point program to rescue the environment, President Nixon issued strict new regulations for auto exhausts in the mid-1970s, proposed encouraging development of a "virtually pollution-free" car by spending $9 million a year on research, and asked for power to phase out the lead in gasoline.

The implications of the increasing clamor have not been lost on Detroit, where a $100 billion-a-year business is at stake.

Henry Ford II, chairman of the Ford Motor Company, in December called environmental pollution "by far the most important problem" facing the auto industry in the 1970s and pledged $31 million for vehicle pollution control in 1970. Only a few weeks later, General Motors President Edward N. Cole told the Society of Automotive Engineers' convention in Detroit that an essentially pollution-free auto could be built by 1980, and added: "We must be highly aggressive in taking action and, equally important, in getting credit for our accomplishments." GM, Ford, and Chrysler each put on major anti-pollution displays for the automotive engineers.

The companies' top executives, who a few years ago scoffed publicly at California's problems (with such wisecracks as, "What Los Angeles needs is filter-tipped people"), are quite circumspect today. GM's Cole even was willing to kick an old ally, the oil business, so as to make the point that lead in gasoline is dangerous and should be removed. Once President Nixon had spoken out against leaded gasoline, GM (followed closely by Ford) swiftly passed the word that it was redesigning the engines on most of its 1971 models so that they would operate on lead-free gasoline.

To understand why Detroit is on the defensive, it is necessary to understand the automobile's role in polluting the air.

The air is ambient—that is, all encompassing. It forms an envelope around the earth to a height of nineteen or twenty miles. Four-fifths of it is in the first seven miles above earth. Man used to consider the air infinite, but it actually is finite, amounting to between five and six quadrillion tons. That amount would seem to suffice for eternity, but many scientists now worry that we are expelling so many poisons into the air so quickly that we are in danger of changing its nature—in which case, "filter-tipped people" may become a necessity.

The draft of a national emissions standards study made for Congress by the National Air Pollution Control Administration (NAPCA) last year said:

"It has been suggested by eminent scientists that the net increase of pollutants such as particulate matter and carbon dioxide in the atmosphere since the beginning of the industrial revolution has affected the weather. Since 1860, fossil fuel burning has increased the atmospheric content of carbon dioxide about fourteen per cent.

"Some scientists fear that increases in carbon dioxide will prevent the earth's heat from escaping into space, melt the polar ice caps, raise oceans as much as 400 feet, and drown many cities. Other scientists predict a cooler earth as the sunlight is blocked by increases in particulates. The results could be more rain and hail and even a possible decrease in the food supply."

Almost four-fifths of the air is nitrogen, almost one-fifth oxygen, the rest other gases and water vapor.

About thirty per cent of the oxygen inhaled by a person goes to the brain. Without it, the brain is fatally damaged within six minutes. The highly specialized tissue of human lungs—an evolution of millions of years —acts as a one-way screen, holding back the blood on one side but permitting the air's oxygen to make its way to the blood, where millions of red cells transport it to other body tissues and exchange the fresh oxygen for carbon dioxide, a waste which is conveyed back to the lungs and exhaled.

Almost everyone knows not to shut his garage doors when his auto's motor is running, but not many people know why.

The reason is that the auto's internal combustion engine emits great quantities of carbon monoxide, a poison which has an affinity for the blood's hemoglobin— the red cells transporting oxygen—about 210 times greater than oxygen. Thus, relatively small concentrations of carbon monoxide can deprive vital body functions of an oxygen supply. The result, as recent studies have confirmed, can be headaches, loss of visual acuity, decreased muscular coordination, loss of energy, blackouts, damage to the central nervous system, and reduced chance of survival from heart attacks.

Fresh air contains less than one-tenth of one part carbon monoxide for each million parts of air. The air in large American cities contains 100 times that amount of carbon monoxide. The bulk of it comes from the internal combustion engines of automobiles.

The best estimates available are that the United States puts about 188.8 million tons of pollutants into the air yearly. The "big five" in pollutants are:

CARBON MONOXIDE, tasteless, colorless, odorless, and lethal. About ninety-four million tons a year go into U.S. air, three-quarters of that from motor vehicles.

SULFUR OXIDES, which in combination with the moist membranes of the lungs form sulfuric acid, a poison. Some 30.4 million tons are expelled into the air yearly, two-thirds from burning coal.

HYDROCARBONS, organic compounds which are vital to the photochemical process by which smog is produced. Some 25.9 million tons go into the air annually, more than half from motor vehicles.

PARTICULATES, tiny bits of matter which become deadly irritants when combined with other pollutants. Some 21.5 million tons go into U.S. air, mostly from smokestacks.

NITROGEN OXIDES, another vital ingredient of smog. About seventeen million tons are expelled into the air each year, slightly less than half from vehicles.

Obviously, automobiles are the chief villains when it comes to carbon monoxide, hydrocarbons, and nitrogen oxides, though they are not wholly blameless in the other two categories. (For instance, autos spew out 200,000 tons of lead particulates annually, as a result of the almost universal practice of selling leaded gasolines to reduce engine knock.)

Even relatively low concentrations of carbon monoxide affect drivers, and peak-hour traffic jams in Los Angeles and Detroit have built up concentrations as high as 150 parts per million or even higher.

Hydrocarbons, on the other hand, seem to have little direct effect on health by themselves. High concentrations of nitrogen oxides may produce lung damage, but this is still only a tentative conclusion.

What is not tentative is the effect of "marrying" hydrocarbons and nitrogen oxides in sunlight: A whole new family of secondary products called oxidants results —irritating eyes, ears, nose, throat, and respiratory system, reducing visibility, damaging plants and materials, impairing lung function in victims of emphysema, even interfering with athletic performance of teenagers. There is also growing suspicion that oxidants have carcinogenic effects.

In Los Angeles, the smog is so bad that doctors advise 10,000 persons a year to leave the area. Eighty per cent of all metropolitan Los Angeles's air pollution is caused by automobiles. The same is true of Washington, D.C., where the number of cars per square mile is one and a half times as great as in Los Angeles.

The internal combustion engine is responsible for the smog, the carbon monoxide, and Detroit's vast business enterprises. The trouble with the internal combustion engine is that it is so popular. In the United States alone, there are ninety million autos and fifteen million trucks and buses on the highways. All but a handful use the internal combustion engine.

The engine burns its fuel within itself. Its carburetor mixes air with gasoline. The mixture is forced into combustion chambers (cylinders), where sparks explode the mixture intermittently, driving pistons. The power produced is transmitted to the wheels.

The problem is the intermittent explosion of the fuel —a process in which the fuel is never completely burned. A briefing paper prepared last August for Dr. Lee DuBridge, head of the White House Office of Science and Technology, reported: "There is strong evidence that the use of Federal standards geared to controlling the internal combustion engine will not result in the drastic inroads on the problem needed to safeguard public health. At best, the effect of present Federal standards will be to postpone in time the upward growth of pollution levels rather than to reverse the trend. . . . These controls [are] far less than adequate to cope with a problem already well out of hand. . . . There is no guarantee that the degree of control that is possible with the internal combustion engine will be adequate. . . . The problem is already beyond reasonable bounds."

Despite such warnings, it appears that the Nixon Administration, under benevolent guidance from the auto makers, is still placing its bets on modification of the internal combustion engine and its fuel. This, at least, was the gist of testimony from Assistant Secretary of Health, Education and Welfare Creed Black to the Senate Commerce Committee last winter during a hearing on a bill introduced by Muskie and the two Democratic Senators from Washington, Warren G. Magnuson and Henry Jackson, to encourage development of a low-emission auto by permitting the Government to pay up to twenty-five per cent above normal prices if the auto proved pollution-free.

GM and Ford, with Chrysler and American Motors trailing far behind, seem to have convinced the White House, HEW, and NAPCA that the internal combustion engine can and should be salvaged. The companies are now willing to invest $80 million to $100 million a year in research, and they are now taking this research seriously.

The odd thing is that the industry has been on notice since the mid-1950s that it would have to do something. By that time Los Angeles County, plagued with smog since World War II, had forced the shutdown of 1.5 million backyard incinerators and, when that failed to clear up the smog, had prosecuted oil refineries, steel mills, and 40,000 other industrial offenders. Nothing worked, the smog got worse, and the automobile was pinpointed as the culprit.

In the late 1950s the auto industry fought California state legislation, but in 1960 the first state law finally passed, requiring only a few simple adjustments in the auto's crankcase. Gradually the state tightened up its requirements and by 1965 the industry could no longer hold off Federal legislation; the 1968 models were the first affected, and all that was required, again, was a fairly simple cutback on carbon monoxide and hydrocarbon emissions.

More stringent Federal controls have been placed on

1970 and 1971 models, and as a result carbon monoxide and hydrocarbon emissions in the 1971 models will be reduced about three quarters from the emissions of those two gases in the pre-1968 models. But the new standards laid down in mid-February 1969 for nitrogen oxides do not go into effect until the 1973 model year, though California—with its stricter controls—is demanding reductions in nitrogen oxides in the 1972 models.

Farther away, in the 1975 model year, the Nixon Administration is demanding its first reduction in emissions of particulates (to a third of the present emissions); further reduction in nitrogen oxides (to a seventh of the present emissions); further reduction in carbon monoxide (to less than half the present standard); and further reduction in hydrocarbons (to less than a quarter of the present standard). The Administration's goals reportedly call for another fifty per cent reduction of the 1975 emissions levels in all categories by 1980.

Achievement of those goals would solve the problem, but there is strong reason to doubt that the goals can be achieved with the internal combustion engine. So far, the chief anti-pollution improvements on the internal combustion engine have taken two forms: Injecting air into the still-hot mixture going out the exhaust system, thus creating more thorough combustion, or regulating the carburetor jet or nozzle that mixes gasoline with air more precisely, so that less fuel goes into the mixture.

The latter method is used on about eighty per cent of new American cars because the former method requires an air pump and is more expensive. Using these two methods—and including the 1971 model year—total air pollution from automobiles will diminish somewhat in the 1970s, but by 1980, NAPCA says, it will be on the increase again because of the growing number of autos on the highways.

The auto makers have dragged their feet for fifteen years. For example, Chrysler has done a considerable amount of research on a turbine engine but maintains a total commitment to internal combustion. One of the big companies developed a catalytic converter in 1964—a device which would go a long way toward more complete combustion of gasoline if gasoline were unleaded—but simply laid it on the shelf; no one wanted to upset a symbiotic relationship with the oil industry. As late as May 1968, Henry Ford II was telling a magazine interviewer that he preferred a cooperative "research and development" program with several oil companies in the fight against pollution.

As for tests with such non-polluting vehicles as the electric car, Ford said: "We have tremendous investments in facilities for engines, transmissions, and axles, and I can't see throwing these away just because the electric car doesn't emit fumes." And when asked what his company's greatest problem was, Ford replied, "That's easy, making more money."

Only eighteen months later, Ford's attitude seemed to have changed radically. What may have helped him along was the Federal anti-trust suit filed ten days before President Nixon took office. The suit accused four big auto companies of conspiring to retard development and use of devices to control auto-produced air pollution. Under a consent agreement, the auto makers—without admitting their guilt—said they would not obstruct development of anti-smog devices and would make available, without fees, licenses of anti-pollution inventions to firms desiring them.

Detroit's new sincerity is verbalized this way by Chrysler's research director, George J. Huebner, Jr.: "There are no holds barred [on the anti-pollution effort]. This is an all-out effort. Maybe people are waiting to see if we will fall on our face. But we are not going to. . . ."

To cut pollution Detroit can install catalytic converters, which it has ruled out because of the gasoline problem, or get a replacement for the internal combustion engine, which it refuses to do for economic reasons, or develop an exhaust manifold reactor, in which exhaust gases are mixed with air and "after-burned" in large, insulated, stainless steel manifolds at high temperatures. Such manifolds will require large amounts of fairly exotic metals, cost $200 to $300 (to be passed on to the car buyer), and require more maintenance than most drivers give their cars. But the afterburners also could represent a huge new market for the auto makers.

There are alternatives to afterburners on the internal combustion engine. One is to reform the engine by direct injection of the fuel into each cylinder, metering the gasoline precisely, eliminating the carburetor, increasing horsepower and economy—and reducing emissions. Volkswagen, Mercedes-Benz, Porsche, and Alfa-Romeo already have begun to build their engines in Europe this way, and there are hints that American manufacturers are working on the same principle.

A more radical alternative is to do away with the internal combustion engine entirely. A number of experimenters and small companies are working to perfect an external combustion or "steam" engine; others are pushing hard to make a practical and economical electric car.

The external combustion engine converts fuel energy into thermal energy of a working fluid. The engine has the singular advantage of burning its fuel much more completely than the internal combustion engine (since the burning is continuous) under low temperatures and pressures. The quantity of carbon monoxide and hydrocarbons emitted from the steam engine is about one-twentieth of the amount emitted from an uncontrolled internal combustion engine. Steam turbines produced so far have shown variable nitrogen oxide emission rates, but most engineers believe there is no inherent barrier to the development of turbines with low nitrogen oxide emissions.

The silent steam engine does not need as much horsepower as the internal combustion engine because it

does not lose as much power. Technically it is further advanced than the electric-powered car. But the steam engine has its drawbacks, too. More expensive metals and more precise tooling (for a closed system) are needed. Some believe the external combustion engine is overweight and accelerates too slowly. But possibly the biggest drawback has nothing to do with the engine itself; it is simply that the auto makers, who have the expertise and large amounts of necessary capital needed to solve the steam engine's remaining problems, also have the greatest vested interest in perpetuating the internal combustion engine.

Nevertheless, the steam engine appears to be the best of the far-out candidates to replace the internal combustion engine, and companies in California, Massachusetts, and Nevada—the last headed by retired millionaire William Lear, who made the business jet a great success—have experimental models in various stages of testing.

Another alternative—even farther out, most experts think—is the electric engine.

Development of a practical battery is still highly problematical, but there is another difficulty: If the nation's automobiles converted to electricity on anything like the present scale of use, demand for power to charge the batteries would soar. That, in turn, would mean building many more coal and oil-fired utility plants—and these are among the worst American industrial polluters.

Both GM and Ford have experimented with, and are continuing to work with, electric engines, the only sure way of getting zero emissions of pollutants from autos. General Dynamics, Gulton Industries, Allis-Chalmers, and Westinghouse have all done work in this specialty, and some smaller firms actually have marketed a few dozen electric cars. But no one is especially sanguine about ending air pollution with electric cars.

A final alternative that is beginning to look much more feasible is use of a different fuel in the internal combustion engine. Either compressed natural gas or liquefied petroleum gas can be burned easily in present motors with relatively simple and inexpensive ($200 to $300) modifications. Mileage is better; so is economy. But again, there are problems.

Though such fuels cut pollution greatly (because the fuels burn much more completely), they must be used under pressure. That means a sealed system which, if ruptured in a mere fender-bender accident, could leak, catch fire, or explode.

The vendors of natural gas and petroleum gas deny that their wares are any less safe than gasoline, and they may be right. The Federal General Services Administration is testing a dozen vehicles on natural gas in Los Angeles and several dozen more in Houston and Mississippi, and has had encouraging experiences so far. Petroleum gas has been used in the municipal fleet of Tampa, Florida, for several years and in Chicago's bus system for more than a decade with success. Indeed, more than 200,000 vehicles, mostly trucks and specialized vehicles such as fork-lifts, have operated for some years on petroleum gas.

But problems of supply and distribution make it likely that these two fuels will be confined to fleets of trucks, buses, taxis, and possibly short-run rental cars.

All of which puts the problem of our fouled ambient air on the Nixon Administration's back again. Within NAPCA only a couple of million dollars yearly have gone to research—most of the agency's $60 million-a-year budget has been spent for establishing a bureaucracy that could set up air quality standards for fifty-seven metropolitan areas and promulgate those standards. Within the Department of Transportation, less than $1 million a year has gone to research, mostly to run a couple of smog-free bus experiments.

GM says it has been spending about $45 million a year on anti-pollution research and development, and Ford has been spending $28 million.

The man most angry about the record is Senator Muskie, who pioneered the early Federal legislation. He believes the Nixon Administration's approach—setting goals for industry which seem fairly distant in time—is exactly wrong. He believes that the only way to achieve results is through "a steady tightening of standards, on a regular and frequent basis, until an emission-free vehicle comes off the assembly line." He predicts that the short-changing of research, both by the Federal executive branch and by industry, will haunt the nation in future years.

Oddly enough, the Republican Governor of California, Ronald Reagan, seems to agree with Muskie. But then, he has heard the birds cough.

Up to Our Ears in Noise

by THEODORE BERLAND

Noise is increasing at an alarming rate. It invades our privacy and interrupts our conversations. It even affects our health by causing eye pupils to widen, blood vessels to narrow, stomachs to turn, and nerves to jump. It can destroy some of the most important cells of the inner ear and cause permanent hearing loss.

Yet we cannot escape it. The noise of radios, television sets, stereo systems, food blenders, garbage disposal units, power tools, and vacuum cleaners fills our homes. The roar of aircraft, motorcycles, air conditioners,

THEODORE BERLAND *is a free-lance science writer. His books include* The Scientific Life, Your Children's Teeth, *and* The Fight for Quiet, *scheduled for publication in 1970.*

power lawn mowers, trucks, and thousands of other noisemakers surrounds us out-of-doors. The once-quiet stillness of a winter day in the forest is shattered by the deafening whine of snowmobiles. Outboard motors reverberate across lake waters, driving away fish and fishermen. Rock music is amplified to such high levels that there is danger of a widespread hearing loss among youth.

As if all of this were not enough, the worst is yet to come in the sound of the ground-shaking thunder-clap of the sonic boom produced by large supersonic airliners. The first of these, *Concorde* No. 001, lifted off a runway at Toulouse in southern France on March 2, 1969. The second was in the air in England five weeks later, and this was followed by the maiden flight of Russia's TU-144, in May. Despite wide concern over the hazards of sonic boom, President Richard M. Nixon gave approval, in September, to the building of a U.S. supersonic transport by the Boeing Company. The shock waves of these planes, nerve-racking and ear-shattering, will be felt along a belt extending 40 miles on each side of the plane's flight path. So far, there is no way to eliminate the boom, which is produced continuously the whole length of the supersonic flight. Its only saving grace is that it will keep reminding us that we are up to our ears in a steadily rising sea of unwanted sound.

Man is an adaptable animal. Without realizing it, he has become accustomed to excessive noise pollution in his environment. But Dr. Alexander Cohen of the U.S. Public Health Service's National Noise Study says, "This sonic boom is not something you adapt to easily."

The problem of noise is best defined in terms of the basic unit used to measure the intensity of sound. This is the decibel, which is a 10th of a larger unit, the bel, named in honor of Alexander Graham Bell. One decibel, or 1 db, is equivalent to the faintest sound that can be heard. It is not a linear unit, such as the inch, but a logarithmic unit. Thus, 10 db is tenfold the power of 1 db, and 20 db is a hundredfold the power of 1 db. The logarithmic scale is necessary because of the incredible range of the human ear. The ear can hear sounds as faint as those produced by a breeze. It is comfortable with the 50 db of a quiet office, but it can also tolerate a subway train screaming through its underground tunnel at 100 db, or a jet plane taking off nearby at 140 db. Some people feel discomfort with sounds of 85 db, but most people do not notice this until the loudness reaches at least 115 db, while they feel pain at 145 db.

The physical basis of noise—sound—can be measured by sound-level meters, portable devices that readily determine the degree of noise. Meters are necessary for an accurate measurement because the human ear has internal adjustments that lessen the loudness of what it hears. The meter measures noise exactly as it is, somewhat as a camera light meter tells us how bright the light is, even though our eyes have automatically adjusted to the brightness.

A noise meter graphically and objectively reveals how noisy our world is. Some authorities say that the noise level is rising at the rate of a decibel a year. Look at—or rather, listen to—our homes. Noisemakers there include roaring garbage disposal units and dishwashers, whining mixers and blenders, and the voices and footsteps of neighbors. As homes become more and more mechanized to reduce the burden of labor, they add to the burden of noise on the human ear.

The kitchen is probably the noisiest room in any house because of its many mechanized noisemakers, and because the hard surfaces of walls and cabinets create more reverberating noises by failing to absorb sound. Dr. Lee E. Farr of the California Department of Health says that we are inadvertently turning our kitchens "into miniature simulators of old-fashioned boiler factories." He found that a kitchen may reach the noise level of a subway or an airport—in the 100-db range.

Noise also shatters what once was the peaceful living

room. It is no longer immune to kitchen noises or to the din of neighbors in other living rooms on the other side of acoustically transparent walls. Add to this television and recorded music (70 to 80 db) and punctuate it with the whir of a vacuum cleaner (80 db), and the level of living room noise becomes unbearable. Bedrooms are quieter, usually in the range of 55 db. Flush an adjoining toilet, however, and turn on the ventilating fan and the noise level jumps to 72 db.

The quiet of our homes is also invaded by noises from the alley or street, such as the clanking of garbage cans, the barking of dogs, and the incessant clatter of motor traffic. Motor vehicles, in fact, create the most pervasive noise in our civilization. Their engines work by a series of properly timed and contained explosions of gasoline and air mixtures. Metal parts whirl and reciprocate at high speed, rubbing, clanking, and vibrating. The spent gases explode through exhaust pipes and roar through mufflers. Gears hum and grind. Tires slap against the pavement and screech when vehicles move at highway speeds. To top it off, cars have raucous noisemakers—horns—to scare already irritated pedestrians out of the way and out of their minds.

Small wonder that noise levels rise beyond 80 db inside most cars and go even higher outside. If cars are noisy, however, trucks are noisier. They have been measured at levels as high as 100 db even at a distance of 100 feet from the edge of a busy highway. Buses are as noisy as trucks. Sports cars create a still greater racket. Motorcycles are the worst offenders, often exposing riders and passers-by to 120 db.

Transportation in the air seems to involve its own noise ratio. The faster the jumbo jet airliners go, the noisier they become and the more widespread their disturbance. Jets create wide swaths of ferocious noise wherever they take off or land. The high-noise area around the John F. Kennedy International Airport in New York, for instance, is 23 square miles. The area contains 35,000 dwelling units, 108,000 residents, 22 public schools, and several dozen churches, all regularly startled and annoyed by the 80- to 90-db screams of jet airplanes.

On-the-job noise is also rising with increased use of machinery. Construction and demolition workers frequently are exposed to sound levels of 90 to 100 db. Factory workers endure ranges of sound from a 118-db average at boilerworks to a 95-db din in print shops.

Levels of Common Noises

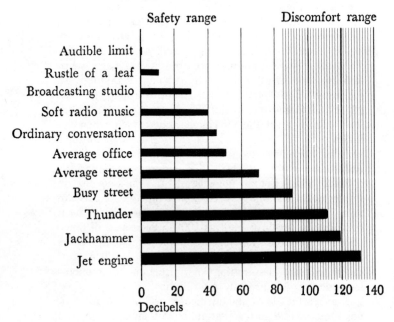

Outdoor workers face similar problems. A survey of Swedish foresters showed that the use of power saws exposed workers to as much as 125 db. Farms, too, have become increasingly noisy, thanks to tractors, harvesters, and milking machines.

While the human ear can handle an incredibly wide range of decibels, the ear may suffer temporary damage if the sound is loud enough. If the loud sound persists for a long time, the damage and the hearing loss can become permanent. Such damage occurs in the complex inner ear where sounds are actually sensed. In this tiny snail-shaped structure, called the cochlea, there are hair cells that can be seen only through a microscope. These hair cells respond to sound waves that pass through the fluid inside the inner ear by bending, much as seaweed bends and sways with the motion of the waves.

The hair cells convert sound into bioelectric signals that are sent along the auditory nerve to the brain. These hair cells become damaged when the sound becomes too intense. They recover, however, if they are given a rest. But if the intensity is repeated before the cells have had time to recover, they can become permanently damaged. The damage, however, is done only to the cells that have been subjected to the frequency of the intense sound waves. Thus, the noise-damaged ear becomes deaf to specific frequencies of sound. It is estimated that more than 16 million people in the United States now suffer from some degree of hearing loss caused by noise. The frequency sensors that go first are usually those used to hear the human voice. Neither hearing aids nor surgery can restore them to normal hearing.

The noises that are most dangerous to hearing are audibly the loudest, highest-pitched, purest in tone, and longest lasting. The first warning sign is a feeling of ear discomfort, and—when the noise is loud enough—pain. This may be followed by a maddening ringing or hissing in the ears, known medically as tinnitus.

Doctors first became concerned about this aspect of human hearing a century ago when they examined boilermakers suffering noise deafness. Since then, doctors have noted a growing assortment of industrial conditions that threaten the ears of workers, the most notorious among them being in textile plants and mines.

Today, noise deafness is a major category of industrial injury, one for which millions of dollars in compensation have been claimed.

Noisy hobbies just as certainly cause deafness as do noisy jobs. The firearms used by hunters and skeet shooters are highly dangerous to the ears because of their very loud (130 db and higher) explosive noises. In this connection, Dr. Jerry L. Northern, chief audiologist at the Walter Reed Army Medical Center, estimates that more than half of the 500,000 men who receive military combat training each year suffer a significant hearing loss.

Rock music, amplified as it usually is to 100 db and higher, has been shown to destroy hair cells in the inner ears of laboratory animals. Add to this the noise of motorcycles and sports cars, and we have what is perhaps the most noise-exposed generation of youth ever in the history of mankind. As one researcher, David M. Lipscomb of the University of Tennessee, points out, "We have apparently reached the point where young people are losing sufficient hearing to jeopardize their occupational potential."

One wag has suggested that record and tape labels should read: "Warning, Modern Music May Be Hazardous to Your Hearing." That is not so far-fetched as it might seem. In fact, a manufacturer of amplifiers for musical instruments uses labels on its equipment to warn that the company "does not guarantee against loss or impairment of hearing due to use of this amplifier."

Noise affects more than the ears. It can affect other parts of the human body as well, particularly the cardiovascular system. Research in both the United States and Europe indicates that noise increases the level of people's cholesterol in the blood and raises blood pressure. German and Italian medical researchers have found that even moderate noises cause small blood vessels to constrict. This vasoconstrictive reflex is the body's automatic way of responding to the stress of noise. It occurs also during sleep, as shown by Dr. Gerd Jansen of Essen, West Germany. He measured vasoconstriction that occurred in the fingers of sleeping subjects when he played recorded noises at only 55 db, the level of nearby traffic. The vasoconstriction took place even when the noise exposure lasted only a fraction of a second. Even with this limited exposure, the blood vessels took minutes to return to normal. Jansen concluded that the sound of traffic at night, heard by sleeping individuals, can endanger their hearts and arteries.

In Italy, Dr. Giovanni Straneo found that noise not only causes the blood vessels in fingers and eyes to constrict, but also has the opposite effect on the blood vessels of the brain. The dilation in the brain could be a reason noises cause headaches. He also found that noise threatens the heart itself by directly altering the rhythm of its beat. In addition, it makes the heart work harder by thickening the blood while constricting its flow in peripheral vessels. One of his associates at the University of Pavia found that noise also increases the stomach's flow of acid.

Other experiments, conducted in West Germany by Jansen, and at the University of Southampton in England, show that even mild noises cause the pupils of the eye to dilate. This helps to explain why watchmakers, surgeons, and others who do close work are especially bothered by noise. Because of the effects of sound, eyes are forced to change focus, thereby causing eyestrain and headache.

Noises we do not hear can also affect us. Some of these, those in the infrasonic range (frequencies below hearing), have been developed as exotic weapons by Vladimir Gavreau in France. The low but powerful, yet unheard, noises produced by his "acoustic laser" and other weapons can actually alter the natural rhythm of brain waves. But his devilish devices are not the only emitters of infrasonic noise. So, too, are ventilating fans, airplanes, and rockets.

Noise provokes our emotions. This psychological

effect is centered on fear and irritation. Everyone re-
acts to the loud noise of a book or glass dropped onto
the floor, or to a sonic boom or other explosion. The
psyche perceives such sudden sounds as warnings of
impending danger. Noise is thus akin to fatigue,
hunger, or chill as a trigger of some biological mechanism of human protection. As some psychologists have
suggested, noise is threatening because it is an invasion
of the living space of others.

Noise also annoys by interfering with thought processes, interposing itself into conversations and daily
activities, and preventing deep sleep. Psychologists point
out that loss of sleep can lead to delusions, hallucina-
tions, and homicidal tendencies.

In 1954, it was noise, in the form of metal fatigue,
that grounded the *Comet,* the world's first jet airliner,
which went into operation in 1952. Noise generated
through the fuselage caused tiny cracks in the metal.
These grew until the fuselage split open and, because
of pressurization, exploded. The metal fatigue caused
it to break—just as a drinking glass will shatter when
it is set into sympathetic vibration by an opera singer's
voice.

A sonic boom is a special kind of noise that, because
it is in the category of explosive, is particularly damaging. It breaks window glass, cracks plaster walls, and
weakens irreplaceable archaeological ruins. Sonic booms
also cause hidden damage, especially to private homes.
This was pointed out by Harvey H. Hubbard, head of
the acoustic branch of the National Aeronautics and
Space Administration. He explained that under the
shock of a sonic boom a house "is forced laterally as a
result of the initial positive loading in the front surface. Then it would be forced inward from all direc-
tions, then forced outward and finally forced laterally
again because of the negative pressures acting on the
back surface."

Though no way has yet been found to reduce the
effects of sonic booms, the effects of most noise can be

alleviated or prevented. We have never made more noise than we are now making, but, at the same time, we have never had as many means for preventing noise and for keeping the level down.

When noise is unbearable, we often protect our ears in a simple way—by covering them with our hands. Earplugs of glass down or even cotton wool are somewhat more effective, but far better are specially designed earmuffs. Some specialists believe that noise is now such a problem that everyone should have his own pocket set of earplugs or ear protectors. These ear protectors could then be used whenever they were needed, much as sunglasses are used to protect the eyes. Some industries make the wearing of ear protectors mandatory. There is no reason why the rest of us who are besieged by noise should not take up such measures voluntarily.

Proper construction techniques can make walls effective barriers to noise, instead of bearers of noise. Soundproof walls essentially rely on the principle of construction that allows each side of a wall to vibrate without transmitting sounds to the other side. This is done by fastening the plaster on each side of the wall to its own 2-by-4-inch studs instead of attaching it to a stud that also connects to the wall of the adjacent room. With this type of construction, noise is not transmitted from one room to another.

Such techniques are being used more and more in new office and apartment building construction. Since quiet construction is more desirable and rentable, many mortgage agencies specify sound-transmission maximums when they loan their money. Another reason is that building codes are slowly being changed to require quiet construction. The most notable of these are New York City's code changes of 1968.

Other measures can be taken, of course, to quiet any home and office. Carpets on the floor above, for instance, absorb the impact sound of shoes. Heavy drapes can be hung on walls and over windows. The drapes not only absorb noise from outside the room, but also absorb interior noises and reduce the reverberation time, which is defined as a "liveliness" that makes room sounds seem to hang in the air. Drapes, carpets, upholstered furniture, and acoustical walls or ceilings all work to absorb sound and to reduce its reflection and reverberation time.

The easiest way to keep noises out is to close all windows and doors and turn on the air conditioner. Calking the windows and weatherstripping the doors help, too. Noisy plumbing can be quieted by inserting cork or neoprene wherever pipes come in contact with studs or other solid structural parts.

Preventing noise, however, is far better than blocking it out, which means that a "think quiet" movement needs to pervade all our technology. A start in this direction has been made by a Bethlehem Steel Corporation noise-control engineer, James H. Botsford, who has developed a steel garbage can that makes a thud instead of a clang when it is dropped. At the Vier Jahreszeiten hotel in Hamburg, West Germany, breakfasts are served on leather trays to prevent dish clatter. There are even quiet pile drivers that work by humming vibration rather than by the banging of a steam hammer. There also are designs for quiet vacuum cleaners and quieter power mowers, but these will probably not be marketed until the public demands them.

It costs much less to reduce the decibels in the early stages of design than it does once a machine is built. A prime example is the jet engine. No attempts were made to deal with the noise problem created by these machines until the 1960s, when the noise of jets overhead became so great that many people began to take their complaints to court. Engine makers responded by adding noise suppressors, but these reduced the thrust of the engines so much that pilots had to add power to compensate and this brought the noise level back to what it would have been anyway. Current efforts to quiet engines on jumbo jets and on airbuses, which

are scheduled to start operations in 1970, consist solely
of lining the inlet ducts with acoustic material. However, this add-on measure may reduce a jet's noise by
perhaps only 10 db. It is probable that more adequate
silencers could have been developed had the engineers
worked on the problem in the early days of jet engine
development.

In the case of supersonic transports, much money and
effort has been expended to test the effects of sonic
booms on buildings and people, but scarcely any research has been aimed at modifying or eliminating the
boom. When the announcement of the approval of the
U.S. supersonic transport was made, in September,
Transportation Secretary John A. Volpe assured the
public that the Administration had ruled out supersonic flights over land until the resultant boom could
be controlled. The plane, therefore, would fly at less
than the speed of sound except over the ocean. Some
aviation experts think that this never-over-land requirement, also the law in some European countries, is so
restrictive as to be a reason to abandon supersonic
transport development until the sonic boom problem is
solved.

Noise that is not or cannot be readily eliminated
often can be contained. Noisy machines can be enclosed
so that the noise does not annoy the entire factory.
Noisy industries can be kept to one part of town and
out of residential communities. Busy streets and highways, and even railroads, can be placed in graded cuts.
This keeps traffic noise largely below grade and confined. Airports can be placed far from towns, and air
traffic can be routed so that planes do not pass over
residential areas on take-off and landing. At the same
time, zoning laws can be used to maintain an industrial
buffer zone between airports and residential areas.

The ultimate solution to our noise problems, as with
many other problems of society, is the law. It forces
people to respect the lives of others, as they should
have, voluntarily, in the first place. Unfortunately, the

progress of the law against noisemakers has been far slower than the acceleration of technology's production of noise. Our legal right to quiet has been confirmed by some courts, but there has been no monumental decision that would help reduce noise levels everywhere. Many people think such a decision is needed now, before the problem becomes even worse.

Some court decisions have favored persons living close to noisy airports, and some states now consider noise as a health threat, one against which noise-deaf workers can claim compensation. However, only six states—California, Nevada, Oregon, Utah, Washington, and Wisconsin—and Puerto Rico require employers to provide, and employees to wear, ear protectors on noisy jobs. No state has a law requiring employers to hold down factory noise to a certain decibel level. The federal government has a 1968 regulation, however, that requires employers on government contracts of more than $10,000 to certify that their employees are not exposed to noise greater than 85 db. The United States lags far behind Austria, Brazil, Finland, Russia, and Sweden, which all have their own laws regulating the amount of noise to which any worker can be exposed.

The Federal Housing Administration (FHA) recommends specific quiet-construction techniques and maximum allowable decibels for all FHA-mortgaged buildings. The recommendations carry weight, but again, other countries—Canada, Great Britain, and West Germany—are ahead of the United States with national building codes, not mere recommendations.

The United States has no general antinoise legislation. In 1960, Britain passed a Noise Abatement Act that allows any citizen to start legal action against a noisemaker. France has a similar law, passed in 1966. Some U.S. cities, such as Chicago and Memphis, have antinoise ordinances, but the enforcement picture is spotty. Memphis, for instance, is quieter than Chicago because the smaller municipality enforces its ordinances more stringently.

It may be that the level of noise production will decrease if we follow a concept presented in 1968 by Charles H. Haar of the U.S. Department of Housing and Urban Development. He suggested that "the airport would lease the right to make noise for a stated period of time, perhaps two or three years. At the expiration of the period, the property owner would be required to prove loss of value suffered due to noise. By settling claims at the expiration of the period, it would be easier to accurately determine the amount of damage, taking into account changes in noise level, up or down, that might have occurred."

Haar was following the lead of a well-known British economist who holds that all citizens have inviolable "amenity rights." These, explains Ezra J. Mishan of the London School of Economics and Political Science, are the rights to peace and quiet, to privacy, and to clean air. In his book, *The Costs of Economic Growth,* he says that the noise created by airlines, factories, and motor vehicles is limited only by what authorities believe the people will put up with. Yet people put up with more and more noise as they get used to it—or think they do. "Clearly," Professor Mishan adds, "if the world were so fashioned that clean air and quiet took on a physically identifiable form, and one allowed it to be transferred between people, we should be able to observe whether a man's quantum of the stuff had been appropriated, or damaged, and institute legal proceedings accordingly."

Laws against noise are not usually passed unless and until the public presses the government for action. Other nations have antinoise laws because they have had antinoise organizations for a much longer time. The Noise Abatement Society, formed in England in 1959, persuaded the government to create a committee that led the fight for the Noise Abatement Act in 1960. An International Association Against Noise, based in Zurich, Switzerland, coordinates the activities of national antinoise groups and holds international conventions

Jet Smoke: Conquest by Camouflage

by WILLIAM E. HOWARD

THE STRATEGY for President Nixon's war on pollution has been cast, and his problem now is to win some battles. Sewer cleaners need to show a little light at the end of the tunnel.

But clear-cut decisions over villainous water and poisonous air promise to be as hard to come by as they have been over the stubborn foe in Vietnam. That it may take years to obtain measurable improvement—and expose his promises to corrosion politically—Mr. Nixon seems only too well aware. For he already has zeroed in on one easy conquest specifically timed to show results to the electorate "late in 1972."

WILLIAM E. HOWARD *is managing editor of the Newhouse National News Service and has done special work in the field of aircraft and air pollution.*

This is the deadline the Administration has imposed on the nation's air carriers in a gentlemen's agreement to extinguish some of the black exhaust plumes so many people complain about from jetliners whistling in and out of their airports.

The agreement applies to approximately one thousand tri-jet Boeing 727s and twin-jet Boeing 737s and McDonnell-Douglas DC-9s—about one-third the domestic commercial fleet. These medium and short range airliners make a high proportion of all takeoffs and landings as they haul the bulk of inter-city traffic around the country, and the airlines are picking up the entire bill—they claim some $15 million—for smoke-reducing modifications to the engines. So it would appear this will be quite a victory to flaunt in the next Presidential campaign, having the virtue of being free to the Government and highly visible as a clean-up step to the public.

But hold on. It won't be all that neat and clean.

Officials of the National Air Pollution Control Administration (NAPCA) acknowledge—reluctantly—a certain "tradeoff" is involved. The reduction in jet smoke (up to eighty per cent), they say, will be won only at the expense of significantly increasing (by forty per cent or more) the jets' output of nitrogen oxide (NOx), one of the prime invisible ingredients in the formation of smog.

Somehow this invisible side effect never got mentioned when Health, Education and Welfare Secretary Robert H. Finch announced the smoke reduction agreement on January 20 after meeting in private with thirty-one airline representatives. A NAPCA technician later conceded this was an "unfortunate omission." But nothing was done to correct it in the press.

Government people on the inside of the air pollution battle become a little uncomfortable when questioned about this bit of camouflage as well as the timing and selective nature of the agreement. They are aware the NAPCA has not established criteria for permissible limits of NOx, which is generated for the most part by automobiles, and won't get them nailed down until February, 1971. The "tradeoff" thus is being made in the dark. Further modifications may be necessary once NOx emission standards are set.

One NAPCA official, in rather lamely defending the decision to move now against this particular group of smoke-makers, told me that "unburned carbon particles from jets are a serious health hazard in the vicinity of airports." (Actually, there are no medical studies available to prove this charge.) I then asked him why, if smoke was such a concern, Finch had exempted the four-engine jets. (They are pretty fair smoke-belchers, too.) His answer was: "But they aren't as bad as the shorter range jets."

A Federal Aviation Administration official was more straightforward. He said the exemption made the agreement "essentially meaningless" as far as New York's Kennedy International, Los Angeles International, and other airports frequented by four-engine jets are concerned. There will be no visible improvement. These jetports, of course, are all situated in metropolitan areas which President Nixon's political strategists have written off anyway. So the only impact of the agreement will be on the smaller airports serving "middle America," which he does care about.

It is interesting that the airlines, already under pressure from several states and cities to abate smoke, had pledged only a week before meeting with Finch to complete modifications of their Boeing 727s and 737s and DC-9s by the end of 1974. The pledge was made to the FAA and pointedly ignored by Finch, who, some airline spokesmen claim, threatened to seek legislation unless they yielded to advancing the modification deadline.

They gave in to Finch only after extracting a reciprocal promise that he would not press for either regulatory or legislative action on pollution controls—a commitment which Mr. Nixon extended to his February 10 anti-pollution message to Congress by omitting any reference to airplane emissions.

This is the really unfortunate aspect of the whole affair; smoke may be obscuring a much worse pollution problem. The NAPCA, in a 1968 report to Congress, lists jet smoke as the least of airliner pollutants. Much higher amounts of carbon monoxide, hydrocarbons, and NOx are emitted during a takeoff and landing. And this is true of piston-engine aircraft. Further, the 130,000 general aviation planes, most of which burn high octane gasoline, spew out lead in their exhaust gases. The NAPCA report says the amount is unknown but lead compounds probably account for half of the particulate emissions from piston engines.

Such favored treatment by the Administration may not stand, however, in any omnibus anti-pollution measure passed by Congress. Democratic Senator Edmund S. Muskie of Maine, chairman of the Senate's Air and Water Pollution Subcommittee and a likely candidate to oppose Mr. Nixon in 1972, has a bill designed to give HEW authority to regulate all jet emissions. And he has said he will press on with it.

Moreover, a number of state officials are upset about aircraft pollution—and not just the smoke plumes. California is delving into the NOx problem and is worrying about carbon monoxide wafting around Los Angeles International Airport. One estimate pegs carbon monoxide (CO) from aircraft as accounting for three to five per cent of all CO emissions in Los Angeles County by 1980 versus a present contribution of less than one per cent.

Court actions are either in progress or under consideration in New Jersey, New York, Illinois, and Massachusetts to speed up and make binding the airlines' smoke abatement program. California has a new law setting January 1, 1971 as the deadline for limiting smoke emissions to forty per cent opacity for up to ten seconds out of any hour.

Thus, pressure is building outside Congress for regulation, Finch and the President notwithstanding. "What teeth does a gentlemen's agreement have?" asks New Jersey Attorney General Theodore A. Schwartz. "We want enforcement."

One of the difficulties in attacking aircraft emissions per se is that they include the same contaminants as highway vehicles and other fossil fuel burning sources. There is no trace element to single them out; they are mingled in the total pollution soup.

One table of emission *estimates* in the 1968 NAPCA report shows all civil aircraft in the United States responsible for 1.2 per cent of the total tonnage of CO in 1967, .7 per cent of hydrocarbons, .1 per cent of NOx, and .1 per cent of carbon particulates.

"If we were half the bastards the auto producers are," grumbled an Air Transport Association spokesman, "then people would really have something to complain about."

These figures are admittedly negligible. But the NAPCA report says not much stock should be put in them; they may be off by "an order-of-magnitude error" because of sampling variations in jet engine emissions. Hence, the actual pollutant factor is unknown today.

Interestingly enough, the Federal Aviation Administration, which plays uncle to the aviation industry, has never looked into the question of airport pollution. It has one pollution study underway now—the effects of tobacco smoke on airplane cabin atmospheres, a study inspired by Ralph Nader.

Yet Transportation Secretary John A. Volpe, under whom the FAA operates, felt qualified to state at the time of the Finch agreement that four-engine jets like the Boeing 707 and DC-8 need not be controlled because they are lesser polluters than the smaller jets. Apparently he did not read the 1968 NAPCA report. The report claims the four-engine jets blow out a little less smoke (2.80 pounds against 3.48 pounds) during a landing-taxiing-takeoff (LTO) cycle, but are more than twice the polluters in every other category. The amount of CO discharged during a LTO for the large planes is 175.5 pounds against 83.7 pounds for the smaller ones; hydrocarbon organics—89.7 pounds against 6.3 pounds; and NO_x—13.24 pounds against 5.78 pounds.

Obviously, the big jets could stand major modification. Whoever engineered their sufferance must be a hero to the airlines. It has saved them many millions of dollars.

The villain singled out in the Finch agreement is the Pratt & Whitney JT8-D engine powering the shorter range jets and is the easiest to fix. It has nine combustors or "burner cans" with interior elements so structured as to allow pockets of fuel to accumulate in a full-power condition. Not all the fuel is consumed in these pockets, producing carbon particles which go into the exhaust as smoke. Pratt & Whitney has redesigned the cans to eliminate the pockets and burn the fuel at a higher temperature for more complete combustion. (Airline spokesmen say they will install them during major engine overhauls.)

It is the hotter temperature, says the NAPCA, which steps up the production of NO_x. CO and hydrocarbon production are not affected and may even be decreased. Though the actual amounts of NO_x do not look significant, health officials are concerned because of the Boeing 747 and other superjets being introduced now and in the next few years. The superjets are expected to increase the output of nitrogen oxides considerably because their "smokeless" engines also run at higher temperatures and because they will use much more fuel while landing and taking off.

In California, state health men are examining the possibility that gains in reducing NO_x emissions from highway vehicles may be offset by the superjets and greater jet traffic. If true, there would be no diminution in Los Angeles' smog and the airlines would qualify as "bastards."

Furthermore, from all official indications the aircraft

pollution problem promises to get worse everywhere in the years ahead. The number of private planes is increasing at the rate of 8,000 per year, and the commercial domestic fleet, now standing at 3,000 planes, keeps growing. By 1980, the NAPCA estimates the annual tonnages dumped on all FAA-controlled terminals will be: CO—1.27 million tons (up fifty-nine per cent from 1967); hydrocarbons—240,000 tons (up eighty-five per cent); NO_x—58,000 tons (up 300 per cent); and carbon particulates—14,000 tons (up 133 per cent). These estimates were made before the Finch agreement. But because it affects only less than one per cent of all civil aircraft and none of the foreign carriers, the agreement will not change the arithmetic much.

The conquest of smoke still adds up to a transparent victory for President Nixon.

A Better World for Fewer Children

by GEORGE WALD

NONE of the things that now most need to be done for our country and for the world have much chance of working unless coupled with the control of population. By present indications our present population of 3.5 billions will have doubled by the end of this century. Long before that, we can expect famine on an unprecedented scale in many parts of the world.

Yet this in itself is not the heart of the problem. If it were, one would have some small reason for optimism; for in the last decade the world's food supplies have increased more rapidly than its population.

The concept that food is the primary problem is a prevalent and dangerous misunderstanding. It implies that the main point of the human enterprise from now

---

GEORGE WALD *is Higgins professor of biology at Harvard University and 1968 Nobel Prize winner in physiology and medicine.*

on will be to see how many persons can be kept alive on the surface of the earth. A distinguished demographer recently estimated that with what he calls "proper management" we could support a world population of forty billions.

Of course, under those conditions people would not eat meat; there would be no place for cows, sheep, or pigs in such a world. This would be an altogether bankrupt view of the human enterprise. Humanity still has a chance at creating an ever wider, richer, and more meaningful culture. This would degrade it to simple production—a meaningless venture in simple multiplication. Even that, however well managed, must come to an end, as the potential resources of the planet become insufficient to feed further numbers of people.

The point then is not how many people one can feed on this planet, but what population can best fulfill human potentialities. One is interested not in the quantity but in the quality of human life. From that point of view the world is probably already over-populated. China and India were once great cultures, enormously creative in the sciences, the visual arts, and literature; but those aspects of Indian and Chinese culture declined centuries ago for reasons associated, I think, with overpopulation.

The Western world also is becoming crowded; I do not think it irrelevant that the quality of our production in the arts has declined greatly in the last century or two. Western science is flourishing, but the productivity of the individual scientist is nothing like what it was up to a century ago. It would take four to six top scientists of the present generation to approach in productivity, scope, and quality the contributions of Charles Darwin, Hermann von Helmholtz, or James Clerk Maxwell. Those men had no labor-saving devices, so far as I know not even secretaries—no dictaphones, microfilm, computerized information, retrieval services, and the like. They did, however, have peace and quiet, the chance to walk through green fields, along quiet rivers, and to find relief from all the crowding, noise, filth, and endless distractions of modern urban life.

A second profound misunderstanding has plagued many earlier discussions of the population problem. This is the widely prevalent view that the poor are over-reproducing, the well-to-do are under-reproducing, and the quality of the human race is hence going downhill. Quite apart from the naive assumption that the economically poor are necessarily also genetically inferior, there are other, almost as serious troubles with this view of the problem.

We are beginning to realize now that it is precisely the well-to-do and their children who make the most trouble—who are at once the biggest consumers and the biggest polluters. That is true individually, and has its national aspects. It is claimed by reliable sources that an American child uses fifty times as much of the world's resources as an Indian child. Our country, which contains only about six per cent of the world's population, uses about forty per cent of the world's resources, and accounts for about fifty per cent of the world's industrial pollution.

So it is essential that we bring world population under control, not only to keep it from increasing further, but if possible cut it down from its present level. That won't be easy or altogether pleasant. Indeed, it will be so difficult that we would be well advised to choose any viable alternative. But there is none. It is that or disaster. We are not being *asked,* but *told* to control world population. That is now our only chance of a meaningful survival. And whatever is done now must be done quickly, not only because the population is increasing so explosively, but because as one consequence the quality of human life has already been eroded. We must be aware of the danger that persons of future generations, even more out of contact than we with the potentialities of a less crowded world, will have lost a wider human view, and will have become unable to help themselves. In that sense we may be the last generation that can save humanity.

So what to do? First, as rapidly as possible make convenient, safe, and cheap—I would rather say free— means of birth control universally available. That, however, will certainly not be enough. I think we must as rapidly as possible make convenient, safe, altogether legal, and cheap—again I would rather say free—means of abortion universally available.

I hope for the early advent of a safe and efficient abortion pill. There are recent reports of encouraging work in this direction, from England and Sweden, with one of the prostaglandins. I think the condition we must try to achieve everywhere and as rapidly as possible is to see to it that nowhere in the world need a woman have an unwanted child. Having got there, we can take stock and see whether that is yet enough. Very likely not; and then we shall have to go on with a variety of other reasonable procedures. We might begin some of those procedures much sooner: for example, legislate tax discouragements rather than incentives for bearing children, particularly beyond the first two.

Many people still have trouble with the thought of

legalized abortion. Of course the Roman Catholic Church is deeply opposed to it. Lately it has at least considered accepting contraception, before officially deciding against it. It seems to me likely that having once opened the question of contraception, it will now prove very difficult to close.

Abortion, however, is not only rejected by the Catholic hierarchy, but apparently also by large numbers of Catholic laymen. They regard abortion as highly immoral, indeed a form of murder.

It is difficult for me to appreciate the morality of that position in view of the present condition of the world's children. If we were in fact taking proper care of children all over the world, raising them with enough food and shelter and clothing so that they had the chance to fulfill their genetic potentialities, then we might have the privilege of feeling that every embryo should be born. As it is, however, the world's population is now mainly held down through infant mortality. What is killing those children is war, famine, disease, and poverty. That is our present condition, one in which we turn the Four Horsemen of the Apocalypse loose upon the children of the earth. Surely we can and must do better than that.

It is not as though we were asked to introduce abortion into a world that is not already practicing it. It is in fact practiced very widely, not only in those few nations where it is legal, but in others where it is illegal, and frowned upon by tradition and religion. Indeed, some recent statistics seem to show that it is particularly prevalent in a number of Roman Catholic countries, in which other means of birth control are not available.

Data on the extent of illegal abortion are difficult to obtain and not altogether reliable. However, a recent study estimates that in France there is one abortion for each live birth; that in Latin America as a whole there is one abortion for every two live births; and that in Uruguay, there are three abortions to each live birth. (Alice S. Rossi, U.S. Public Health Service, writing in *Dissent,* July-August, 1969).

In numbers of underdeveloped countries, through ignorance, poverty, and the low state of technology, abortion is the principal method of birth control. A lot of this happens under brutal circumstances. The women do it to themselves, or to one another, or at best with the help of some self-taught midwife. All of them suffer, and many of them die. It is one of the penalties of poverty. What goes as morality, in this as in so many other things, sits more lightly on the well-to-do. The poor must bear it in suffering and terror, and at times must pay for it with their lives.

It is precisely a high concern for human life, and most of all for children and what becomes of them, that makes me believe that we must achieve as rapidly as possible universally available, and preferably free, birth control and abortion. Being born unwanted is no favor to any child. Being born to hunger, want, disease, and the ravages of total war is no favor to any child. We need to make a world in which fewer children are born, and in which we take better care of all of them.

So that is my program: *a better world for fewer children.*

Death Sentence

The most savage, immoral, and heartbreaking form of population control is to permit children to enter the world sentenced to death in their earliest years. But this is the fate known to await millions who would never be conceived if birth control were practiced throughout the world to the degree that the planet's limited resources of food and arable land require.

Until a moral and sane approach to birth control *is* adopted, death awaits millions of infants and children. For as U.N. Secretary General U Thant said recently, there are more sick, undernourished, and uneducated children in the world now than there were ten years ago, and "the next ten years will find the number of neglected children increased by millions" unless the international community undertakes a massive effort to prevent it.

Three-quarters of the world's children—nearly a billion—live in developing countries, U Thant pointed out. Using data on these countries compiled by U.N. agencies, he disclosed:

¶ One hundred children are born every half-minute in these areas, and twenty of them will die in their first year.

¶ Of the eighty who survive, sixty will have no access to modern medical care during their childhood. Sixty of the eighty will be malnourished, with the possibility of irreversible physical and mental damage.

¶ Only a little more than half of those who survive to school age will ever set foot in a classroom. Fewer than four out of ten of those who do enter school will complete the elementary grades.

U Thant said that the death rate of children in the one to five age groups is ten to fifty times higher in the developing than in the developed countries.

In spite of the appalling infant mortality rates in the developing countries, and in the face of what birth control efforts do exist in these areas, their total population, according to U Thant, is expected to increase by a half billion during the 1970s.

—THE EDITORS of *The Progressive*

The Population Challenge of the '70's: Achieving a Stationary Population

by RUFUS E. MILES, JR.

RUFUS E. MILES, JR., *is Director of the Mid-Career Program at Princeton University's Woodrow Wilson School of Public and International Affairs. A long-time member and trustee of the Population Reference Bureau, he is currently Chairman of the Bureau's Board of Trustees.*

"Whose Baby is the Population Problem" by Rufus E. Miles, Jr., in Population Bulletin *Vol. 26, No. 1, February 1970. (Washington, D.C.: Population Reference Bureau, 1970). Used by permission.*

Of the four reasons for the deterioration of our environment [pollution, pesticides, population growth, and economic growthmania], population growth is regarded by most people as being least subject to intelligent human control. Influencing birth rates by national policy has been tried in other nations and has been found extremely difficult. The question is, what are our options? If the population problem is as important as we assert, who is going to take responsibility for doing something about it, and what can and should be done? Whose baby *is* the population problem?

Let us examine the alternatives.

THE SCIENTIFIC SOLUTION

We live in what may be the waning days of simplistic faith in science and technology. Yet many people still retain a hope that somehow science will solve our population problem before we become a human anthill. It would be an enormous relief if such hope were well founded, but it isn't.

There are certain things scientists can do and others they cannot. Continued research into the means of fertility control is the crux of their potential contribution. We have every reason to hope that more and better research will yield a wider variety and possibly safer and more reliable methods of fertility control. Scientists may even find a method which is acceptable to the principal religious groups which now oppose the use of contraceptives. Public and private support for such research is substantial and important.

Nevertheless, if scientists were to develop a new means of fertility control with "ideal" characteristics, the basic question would remain: How will people elect to make use of such a scientific advance? If they use it but continue to have appreciably more children than are needed for replacement, the problem of how and when birth and death rates will be brought into balance would remain. Scientists would then be impotent. Even in an autocratic state, it would not be the scientists but the government which would face the problem of what to do. If coercion were the answer, further scientific discoveries would not be needed. Compulsory sterilization would be one obvious means of enforcing a coercive population policy. However, not even the most authoritarian of societies has contemplated such extreme action.

The further potential of agricultural scientists to relieve population pressure in underdeveloped nations is worthy of comment. If scientists should find more effective ways of enlarging the world's food supply, as they have done again and again during the past century, they might provide at best a temporary reprieve. Even on the dubious assumption that their effort involved no further environmental damage, it could only briefly defer the unavoidable necessity of achieving a zero rate of population growth. Genetics, agronomy, and chemistry cannot much longer increase yields per acre at rates which will expand the world's food supply faster than the current two percent annual rate of world population growth. In classical Malthusian terms, then, the effort to stave off malnutrition in the developing nations is getting harder and harder. Should this effort finally collapse, the suffering among the world's hungry majority would reach such an unprecedented scale that it would impel national societies in the direction of more authoritarian governments.

Moreover, as we learn more about the hazards of insecticides, irrigation, and fertilizer runoff, we discover that many of our so-called advances in the production of food and the reduction of disease are, in fact, obtained at the high cost of poisoning our environment. Lake Erie's death can be attributed in part to the profligacy with which we have used fertilizers. Vast areas of the world have been salted into wastelands by improvident irrigation. And DDT, a persistent poison, has circled the globe and found its way into all our bodies.

For a century and a half, agricultural scientists have done a monumental job of postponing Western man's need to face up squarely to the old Malthusian imperatives. Yet through their ecological delinquency, these same scientists are *speeding up* the arrival of new, subtler imperatives—those of environmental decay. We thus face a paradox. The "Green Revolution" has been advanced as a means of buying time against starvation; it may actually be *losing* time for the entire human race.

When the problem of population pressure is examined diligently, it is clear that it is not going to be solved by scientists. It is a nonscientific problem. The question is not whether births and deaths will be brought into balance, but when and how and at what level. This is a problem for each nation to decide. Each will answer it differently, depending on its economic status, political institutions, cultural traditions, and other factors. Controlling population is primarily an economic, cultural and political problem, not a scientific one.

FREEDOM OF CHOICE

"The opportunity to decide the number and spacing of children is a basic human right," says the 1966 United Nations Declaration on Population. This statement means different things to different people. It was written to encourage the provision of family planning services throughout the world. The hope of its proponents was that if extensive family planning services were provided in the less developed countries, they would markedly assist in bringing down birth rates. But the declaration is worded in such a way that it can be, and has been, approved by persons who favor large families and high birth rates. It contains no expression of desire to lower birth rates.

The "freedom of choice" approach is also the domestic policy of the United States. It was originally expressed by President Lyndon B. Johnson in his 1966 Health Message to Congress. . . .

The policy was restated by President Nixon in his "Presidential Message to Congress on Population" on July 18, 1969, but the tone and emphasis were different:

"Finally we must ask: How can we better assist American families so that they will have no more children than they wish to have. . . One of the ways in which we can promote that goal is to provide assistance for more parents in effectively planning their families. . . . Unwanted or untimely childbearing is one of several factors which are driving many families into poverty or keeping them in that condition. Its threat helps to produce the dangerous incidence of illegal abortion. And finally, of course, it needlessly adds to the burdens placed on all our resources by increasing population."

Neither President Johnson nor President Nixon has at any time suggested that people who want and can afford large families should be affected by any considerations other than their own desires, nor have they proposed that the government should exercise leadership in slowing and eventually stopping the growth of the U.S. population. A careful reading of President Nixon's words, however, gives some hope that a significant change may be in the offing. The statement "needlessly adds to the burdens placed on all our resources by increasing population" conveys a very clear impression that the President believes increasing population has become more of a burden than a national asset. . . .

Nevertheless, as recently as February 1970, the U.S. government was still hoping to accommodate, rather than slow down, the projected rate of population growth in this country. It was still following the approach which has guided the Planned Parenthood Federation ever since Margaret Sanger founded this organization in 1916. The goal is to permit married couples to choose consciously and freely whether and when they wish to have children. This is a family planning policy, a freedom-of-choice policy, but not a population policy. . . .

Many of the proponents of this federal policy hope it will appreciably reduce the rate of U.S. population growth. But if they imagine that it alone will slow population growth rapidly enough to avoid extremely adverse consequences to our environment and our society, their assumptions are open to question.

In a memorandum to the National Academy of Sciences in 1967, converted into an article for *Science,* Kingsley Davis . . . concludes that if we are to achieve a zero rate of growth in the foreseeable future, we must do more than rely upon the distribution of free contraceptives to the poor (who are almost exclusively the target group in U.S. family planning programs). We

Percentage Share of Annual U.S. Births, 1960-1965 Average

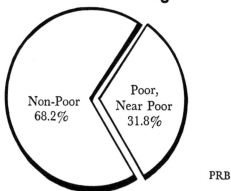

Non-Poor
68.2%

Poor,
Near Poor
31.8%

PRB

Source: Campbell, Arthur. "The Role of Family Planning in the Reduction of Poverty." *Journal of Marriage and the Family,* Vol. 30, No. 2, 1968. Derived from special tabulations by the Bureau of the Census from the *Current Population Survey,* March 1966.

must devise ways of changing individual and social attitudes, governmental policies and incentives, and through these, the motivation of young people and adults in all socioeconomic groups. . . .

Most Americans labor under the illusion that the continued growth of the U.S. population is caused by poor people who have large families, and that if the poor had families of the same size as the non-poor, we would have no significant population problem. *The fact is that much more than half the population increase in this country is contributed by non-poor families who regularly practice contraception.*

Although "unwanted" births pose a significant problem, the contracepting middle class desires more children per "completed" family than the average of 2.2 needed for replacement. As Adolph Schmidt, U.S. Ambassador to Canada, has said: "The major problem is not the *'unwanted* child' but the *'wanted* child.' " . . .

MUTUAL COERCION

It is hardly surprising that the collective result of individual decisions by adult Americans operating on a freedom-of-choice basis, influenced by the traditional ideal of the large family, the growthmania of business, advertising and the profession of economics, is a continuing increase in the U.S. population in the order of one percent per year. At this rate the United States would gain another 100 million people by the year 2010—a date which is only as far in the future as the beginning of the Great Depression is in the past.

To those who believe something more needs to be done than to allow the free market and the freedom-of-choice system to continue on their way, two primary alternatives suggest themselves. Either the freedom-of-choice principle must be abandoned or the influences upon parents and children must be changed. Each alternative deserves careful analysis.

Conceivably, family size could be regulated by fiat, such as permitting families to have a specified number of children and enforcing required sterilization when each family reaches its maximum allowance. Other less drastic forms of coercion could be devised. Whatever the form, the concept of coercion in the regulation of family size is startling and alien to the American people. Nevertheless, it has been very seriously advanced as our only salvation.

The case for "mutual coercion, mutually agreed upon," has been forcefully made by Garrett Hardin. In his 1968 presidential address to the Pacific Division of the American Association for the Advancement of Science, . . . Hardin makes use of an illustration by William Forster Lloyd (1794-1852) which describes the consequences when a group of herdsmen uses a large pasturage as "a common." Each herdsman seeks to maximize his gain. When grazing on the commons reaches the maximum density short of environmental deterioration, each herdsman asks himself whether he should add one more animal. He calculates that one more animal will benefit him positively more than it will reduce the food supply for his share of the total herd. Since all herdsmen act upon such "rational" calculations, the final effect is severe overgrazing and the irreparable ruination of the commons. Tragedy then descends upon all the herdsmen.

The lesson of the commons seems simple and clear. Mutual agreement to limit the number of animals upon a limited land area—an agreement supported by coercive sanctions when necessary—is imperative to avoid collective tragedy. Since men are capable of "overgrazing" their land, water, and air in many more ways than lower animals, the analogy of coercive action to limit the number of human animals seems obvious. Numerous examples of human "overgrazing" of various components of the U.S. environment can be adduced. Our environment is unquestionably deteriorating. . . .

The analogy of the commons is based upon an assumption that each "grazer" is free to decide whether he will increase his use of the commons, and that it will always be in his best economic interest to do so. But children are no longer economic assets as they once were in agrarian economies, particularly those with expanding frontiers. In today's "post-industrial economy," children are expensive pleasures; they are economic liabilities rather than assets.

Most married couples believe that children will afford them psychological satisfactions for which they are willing to pay. Some feel that the absence of children will cause them psychic strains and embarrassments which they are willing to pay to avoid. The psychic rewards of parenthood seem especially important to persons who are deprived of either the satisfactions which come from steady employment or those which come from adequate social and recreational contacts. In any event, since children are economic liabilities, the willingness of adults to deprive themselves of a portion of their economic income to achieve this particular form of psychic satisfaction has nothing in common with the willingness of herdsmen to add to their flocks.

There is no conflict, therefore, between the economic self-interest of married couples to have small families and the collective need of society to preserve "the commons." It is in both their interests to limit procreation to not more than a replacement level. Unfortunately, couples do not seek their self-interest in economic terms alone, but in terms of total satisfactions. They are "buying" children and paying dearly for them. The problem, therefore, is compounded of how to persuade couples to act more in their own economic self-interest and that of their children; how to assist them in obtaining more psychological satisfactions from sources other than large families; and how to replace the outworn and now inimical tradition of the large family with a new "instant tradition" of smaller families. This is an entirely different problem than that of the herdsmen on the commons.

Even if we were to place the broadest possible construction on Hardin's analogy and substitute the concept of general self-interest for that of economic self-interest, his conclusion that we need "mutual coercion, mutually agreed upon" runs up against an almost insuperable obstacle in a representative democracy such as ours. Coercion requires laws with appropriate sanctions, and laws vary in the degree of support needed for their enactment. . . .

It seems abundantly clear that any bid to coerce the regulation of family size would today be opposed by an overwhelming majority of Americans and, looking ahead, it would be opposed by a very substantial group of persons who would fight such legislation with all the emotional force at their command. Under such circumstances, any suggestion that we adopt "mutual coercion, mutually agreed upon" seems hardly to fall within the art of the possible. Non-coercive measures are the only forms of legislation which have any reasonable chance of enactment in the 1970's and 1980's.

REDIRECTING SOCIETY'S MOMENTUM

There appears, then, to be only one viable approach to the population problem in the United States. This is the long, uphill route of encouraging the American people to modify their basic attitudes and behavior so that instead of idealizing large families in the abstract and creating them in flesh and blood, we will prefer small ones and act upon our preferences; so that instead of promoting forms of economic growth which will increasingly pollute our living space, we will insist that we clean up as we go, no matter what the cost; so that instead of measuring our welfare by the amount of our consumption, we will become deeply concerned about enhancing the quality and preserving the variety of life in its numerous forms. These goals require a change in the momentum of our society. They require, among other things, a societal consensus to stop the growth of the U.S. population within a generation and possibly sooner.

Changing the momentum of society sounds next to impossible. But at this very instant it is already undergoing a profound change. The question is, what will its new direction be? . . .

It is clear that a stationary U.S. population will be accepted as an idea whose time has come only if the relatively few individuals and institutions who now see the goal devote their time and resources to gaining widespread understanding, support and governmental action. Private individuals, private nonprofit organizations, and educational institutions will be the key to success or failure in this effort. Waiting for the federal government to take action is like waiting for oneself to act. The government needs a broad base of support before it can move. Writing one's Congressman now will be of little avail, for not a single bill designed to achieve a stationary U.S. population now awaits the disposition of Congress.

For those who would adopt zero population growth as an important and urgent idea, what forms of nourishment can they give it? First, they can join with others who share the same conviction and obtain the mutual reinforcement which comes from discussion, interaction, and organizational activity. Secondly, they can think through the successive steps that will bring about a stationary population, and they can set forth the economic and social repercussions which might ensue, along with proposals for absorbing them into our institutions and mores. And thirdly, when they have arrived at conclusions about achieving and adjusting to zero growth, they can convey their insights to others and devote their time and money to supporting kindred organizations. This is the most difficult and important step in the process of converting a seminal idea to living institutional forms. . . .

THE TWO-CHILD FAMILY

If we are to arrest the growth of U.S. population by the end of the century, the two-child family must voluntarily become the norm. Today an average of just under 2.2 children per completed family is required for replacement, but if the socially accepted norm were two children, the number of families which exceeded two would probably be more than those which had less than two, and the result might come close to replacement. In any event, we cannot expect to achieve the replacement birth rate of 220 children per 100 completed families either quickly or precisely.

The achievement of a consensus on the norm of a two-child family may prove to be extraordinarily difficult. But one factor is obviously favorable: the convergence of personal self-interest in economic terms and the broader societal interest. In most matters where people are appealed to by the leaders of their society or by their government, there is a conflict between personal economic interest and the action required to support the appeal. If, however, young and adult Americans can be encouraged to understand more clearly than most of them already do the future costs of raising a family, and if they are simultaneously told by an increasingly strong chorus of voices of recognized leaders that two-child families would, in the aggregate, be best for the nation's future, we may witness a profound change in U.S. attitudes and mores within a generation. . . .

SOURCES OF LEADERSHIP

The beginnings of the necessary leadership already exist in various private, nonprofit organizations. More such leadership and possibly the means of financing it might emerge if President Nixon's proposed "Commission on Population Growth and the American Future" should discuss in earnest the desirability of achieving a stationary U.S. population. Among the American people there are certainly persons with leadership potential who wish they could earn a living by pursuing their conviction that a zero growth rate is essential to stem the degradation of our physical and social environments.

Until and unless governmental support for such people becomes available, private individuals and private nonprofit and educational organizations must fill this urgent and obvious need.

School and College Curricula

One of the most hopeful and essential means of bringing birth rates down to the replacement level is to introduce this entire subject into the curricula of schools and colleges. If students are to cope with the complex world which they will soon govern as leaders and voters, no more important subjects can be set before them than the growth of human populations, the deterioration of our environment, the decline of many social services, the erosion of personal and political freedom, and the relationships among all these trends. . . .

Institutes for Ecological Study

Institutes for ecological study are emerging in various universities as ecology outgrows its concentration on natural areas remote from human influence. Ecologists now realize that they must study, and study fast, the diverse relationships between man and his *total* environment. Through the eons of time, the dynamic balance of nature—the ecologist's center of attention —has been continually changing, and its largely gradual shifts have seldom caused the simultaneous extinction of numerous species. But we are just beginning to realize that man has caused extremely rapid and radical changes which have produced cataclysmic results. The survival of countless organisms, including man himself, is at stake.

In the September 1969 issue of *Harper's,* John Fisher proposed the creation of a whole university which would study the environmental factors essential to man's survival. It is an intriguing idea, but it would be even more effective if all existing major universities set up interdisciplinary institutes devoted to this concept. Ecology, resource management, the politics and economics of conservation and pollution control, demography and geography in their broadest sense, and other studies focused on the common theme of enhancing man's living space and heightening his ecological awareness deserve even greater emphasis in the 1970's and 1980's than space exploration received in the 1960's. If this new emphasis should emerge, it is a virtual certainty that one major condition of human survival which would be stressed by ecologists and their confreres would be a zero growth rate (and conceivably a slow rollback) of human populations. Ecology and demography should launch an ecumenical movement—a goal which is presently sought more by ecologists than by demographers. . . .

CONSERVATION ORGANIZATIONS

The largest aggregations of people in the country who are organized and committed to prevent further deterioration of the environment are found in the various conservation organizations. Those people can and should be drawn into a closer understanding of the need to stop the growth of the U.S. population. Some of them have already moved to incorporate in their educational programs the objective of at least slowing population growth. Today they can profitably use research materials for discussion and education on achieving a lower or stationary growth rate and on the ways in which the climate of social opinion can be changed toward this end.

COMMISSIONS AND CONFERENCES

The President's proposal for the creation, by Congress, of a Commission on Population Growth and the American Future seems certain to be enacted. It is to conduct a two-year study with an interim report after one year. If its membership chooses, the Commission can give careful attention to establishing a target date (or decade) for achieving a stationary population within the United States. Nothing in the President's Message to Congress on Population either encourages or discourages such a course of action. The way is thus open for putting this subject on the agenda if enough interest is shown by concerned citizens. It would be most unfortunate not to have the Commission give the most thoughtful consideration to this topic.

A privately sponsored "First National Congress on Optimum Population and Environment" is scheduled for June 7-10, 1970, in Chicago. It will bring together representatives of a wide variety of disciplines. While its recommendations will have no official status, they will hopefully be well-formulated and cogent enough to stimulate widespread discussion and exert some degree of influence upon both individual and official attitudes.

Organized local discussion groups leading up to and following such national conferences are important elements in bringing about shifts in private attitudes and public policies.

CLOSING CONSIDERATIONS
POLLUTION AND THE BIRTH RATE

The worldwide drop in birth rates during the Great Depression of the 1930's is highly indicative of a general human behavioral pattern. When families have achieved an advanced standard of living, they are very reluctant to give it up. Thus, should their income drop, they first eliminate expenses which they do not consider essential to their traditional mode of living. One such expense is additional children. Fertility rates in the United States fell to an all-time low during the Depression years. In the minds of most married people, protecting one's standard of living takes precedence over having a large family.

If there should be a decline in the American family's income as a result of a strong antipollution drive (coupled with other costly outlays for improved public services of all kinds, since many have deteriorated below the level of tolerability), the effect would probably be a further diminution in the birth rate. Even if the cumulative effect of these outlays should be a substantially lower rate of increase in real income rather than an outright decline, the birth rate would probably fall in response to the pocketbook squeeze. A "pay-as-we-go" policy in respect to our environment could therefore be doubly beneficial.

INTERNATIONAL IMPLICATIONS

Because of America's high rate of production, consumption and waste disposal, 205 million Americans are depleting the world's resources and polluting the natural environment more than the 2.5 billion inhabitants of the less developed nations. Conservative estimates indicate that the average child born in the United States will put at least 25 times as much stress on the environment as the average child born in India. The "environment" is not confined to the neighborhood or even to the nation in which each individual lives. Nor are the use of scarce and irreplaceable resources and the pollution of the biosphere a neighborhood or national matter; these assaults on the environment are worldwide in scope. They are certain to generate an increase in international frictions, of which we already have a more than ample supply. . . .

A concerted effort to achieve a stationary U.S. population could thus have an important effect internationally. The less developed nations have not established policies or targets which explicitly seek stationary populations within a specified period of time, let alone

U.S. Share of World Consumption and Production, Selected Minerals, 1967

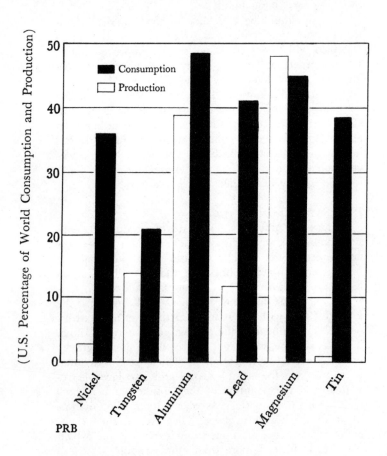

PRB

The wealthier a population, the more it taxes the world's natural resources. As U.S. real per capita income rises, so does the nation's dependency on mineral imports from abroad.

Source: Statistical Abstract of the United States 1969, U.S. Department of Commerce.

programs which have some possibility, however remote, of achieving such a goal. A serious effort by the United States to set its own house in order and develop the various methodologies required to bring birth rates into balance with modern low death rates might have a far greater impact on other nations than all our offers of technical assistance in the limited field of family planning. Meanwhile, without a genuine effort by the United States to bring its own growth rate down toward the zero point, both the credibility and the motives of this country in seeking to persuade other countries to curb their population increases are suspect.

WHOSE BABY?

Evidence is accumulating that if man does not make a quantum jump in the perception of his own self-interest, his very survival may be in peril. A limited human population can, hopefully, learn to live peaceably with itself and with the fauna and flora of the earth in whose kinship all men have evolved. A continued increase, without letup, beyond our present massive population levels is masochistic and suicidal. Consuming the earth's bounty at feverish rates, paying no heed to nature's balances and to the interdependence of all living things, is a formula for human extinction. That man is already consuming more than his share of nature's abundance is evident by the continuing and escalating extermination of hundreds of species of fauna and flora. That man is crowding and contaminating his environment to a point where the quality of his own existence and his enjoyment of life are rapidly deteriorating is self-evident on every hand.

Unless all those who are deeply concerned about man's fate convert their convictions into programs designed to stem the growth of the U.S. population as rapidly as feasible and hopefully well before it reaches

Nuclear Pollution and the Arms Race

by DAVID R. INGLIS

BOTH THE arms race between the nuclear giants and the rapid growth of industry are making appalling inroads on our environment. The manufacture and testing of nuclear weapons add to the world's burden of radioactive contamination, while industrial activity, stimulated by the arms race and civilian demand, belches noxious contaminants into the atmosphere and water courses.

Yet in our ardor for preserving the environment we must not forget that there is a far more compelling reason for putting a lid on the arms race, namely, reducing the risk of nuclear war.

DAVID R. INGLIS *is professor of physics at the University of Massachusetts. Previously he was engaged in research on the theory of nuclear structure at Argonne National Laboratory. He is a frequent contributor to scholarly journals.*

The direct way to modify the arms race is by negotiation and wise example. It is our country that has principally fired the nuclear arms race by insisting on being way ahead in most categories. Our overkill is such that we could afford to set an example of moderation and watch for reciprocal restraint on the other side. The U.S. negotiation stance at the Vienna arms reduction talks should be one of initiative to attain substantial mutual limitations and reductions, rather than one of stalling until we get ABMs and MIRVs before talking seriously.

The recent sudden shift of liberal concern from the ABM to the environment seems to be leaving a vacuum where pressure is urgently needed to stop the arms race by diplomacy and restraint.

The way President Nixon has hopped on the environment bandwagon with enthusiastic words, if little substance, suggests he may have sensed its importance in weakening the opposition that was nearly successful last time, as he seeks to step up the ABM program. With the perpetual expansion of the military establishment, nuclear weapons production is likely to grow, increasing radioactive pollution at home and around the world, strengthening the military-industrial complex, and moving mankind closer to the full horror of nuclear war.

Concern for the environment, and even legislation protecting it, can mildly shackle some of the details of weapons production, but only a change of foreign policy can stop it. The basic shortcoming of the President's budget message was that it called for no really substantial transfer of funds from Vietnam and the arms race to the anti-pollution effort, and gave no indication of an intention to taper off the arms race and make this transfer possible in the future.

The production of nuclear materials—plutonium, tritium, and separated uranium—involves the production of enormous amounts of radioactive materials that must be disposed of as waste, and in the production of power which ends up by heating rivers and lakes enough to affect aquatic life. Furthermore, the uranium separation consumes a lot of power generated by burning coal. It is the disposal of radioactive wastes that is the most serious problem nuclear power presents to the environment. Nuclear materials are produced to fuel both the arms race and the electric utilities industry. The needs of both threaten the environment in a cumulative way.

The most dramatic effect of the arms race on the environment came from the testing of nuclear weapons in the atmosphere in the era before the partial test ban of 1963. Radioactive fission products in unprecedented quantities were carried high in the atmosphere by the mushroom clouds of the big H-bomb explosions, and gradually settled over much of the earth. Yet people went about their daily lives without noticing any tangible or identifiable effects on the environment. We normally live with a weak exposure of radiation from cosmic rays and from ordinary rocks. In terms of this natural background, the increase of overall radiation was not large and some authorities scoffed at misgivings. The normal background causes some cancer and genetic change, and a slight increase could not be easily isolated and recognized.

Yet this oft-quoted comparison with natural background is unfair because the fission process, that which takes place in bomb explosions and in electric power generating reactors, does not merely increase the background radiation. It produces kinds of radioactive substances that are different and which settle in and attack the human body in specific ways, unlike the natural background radiation. Rocks and cosmic rays provide a natural background of gamma rays (deeply penetrating X-rays) and less penetrating beta-rays (electrons) that pass through the whole body indiscriminately, causing weak ionization on the way; cosmic rays passing through the atmosphere also make a special radioactive substance, carbon-14, that becomes rather generally distributed through body tissues. But the fission process creates new types of radioactive atoms that do not exist in nature, and that are dissipated through the air (and water and food supplies) until they settle in the body. Depending on their chemical nature, some of them locate preferentially in certain sensitive parts to do their radioactive damage in a concentrated fashion. Thus, while the overall radiation dosage may be raised only a few per cent by bomb test fallout, the biological damage is disproportionately serious.

During the course of nuclear bomb testing, the danger of one particular element of fallout, strontium 90, was initially denied by Federal Government spokesmen. Its threat was first established by university scientists in independent research. Strontium 90 has a long-lived radioactivity. It is chemically similar to calcium and settles in bone. It concentrates particularly rapidly in the fast-growing bone of fetuses and young children. It gets there by settling on grass eaten by cows and is concentrated in milk. Starting in St. Louis, and then more widely, records have been kept of strontium 90 in the teeth normally lost by children, as well as in fetal skeletons. As a radioactive part of the bone, within which blood is made, strontium 90 can cause leukemia and other forms of cancer. It also attacks the genes, and can cause birth defects and infant death. Yet these maladies arise also from other causes and one cannot pinpoint which cases are caused by the arms race. Invisible though the fallout was, we are well rid of the insidious atmospheric testing which might have been much heavier by now if we had had no test ban.

We should be eager to preserve and extend the test ban. Instead, after all our early worries about the Russians, it is we who are callously breaking it. Of more than two hundred U.S. underground tests, seventeen have vented seriously and the radioactivity from two has been officially reported as observed in Canada. Further pressure to abandon the test ban is apt to come with the growth of the ABM system.

Yet even without nuclear war and without nuclear testing, the arms race still has its effect on the environment through the preparation of nuclear materials. The mine and uranium mill tailings—the waste products—are themselves a serious local danger. They expose ores that were once locked underground to leaching by rain and consequent radioactive pollution of our rivers. But this is still only an accelerated recirculation of nature's radioactivity, mainly that of radium with its slow and therefore relatively weak decay.

More serious are the new man-made radioactive elements, by-products of the reactors that make plutonium and tritium for bombs. Some of these have lifetimes that are short enough to make the immediate radiation intense and yet long enough that they create a hazard for tens or hundreds of years, such as strontium 90 and cesium 137, which have half-value decay times of about thirty years. This means that after a hundred years, they would still be about one-tenth as radioactive as now and still a grave hazard in view of the huge amounts being put in perpetual-care storage.

Some of the nuclear reactors are operated for the Federal Government exclusively for the production of bomb materials. Such plants are at Hanford, Washington (the site of the original wartime plant), Paducah, Kentucky, and Savannah River, South Carolina.

Still other nuclear reactors are owned and operated by the electric utilities industry under Government subsidy for the dual purpose of producing plutonium (much of it for bombs) and electric power.

The subsidies provided by the Atomic Energy Commission at the taxpayers' expense take several forms. One is risk insurance. The Federal Government pays for most of what limited insurance coverage there is, and beyond that lets the public take the risk of the possible consequences of a serious reactor-runaway accident.

As another form of subsidy, the Government runs the huge, expensive, energy-consuming, thermal-diffusion plants. These supply the enriched uranium used as fuel in the industrial reactors at a favorable price to industry. A third form of subsidy is the guaranteed price at which the Government will buy all the plutonium industry produces. It is hoped that plutonium as well as enriched uranium will be used to fuel future reactors, but we do not yet know how.

The only current use for plutonium is for bombs. Both because this subsidy was necessary to make the rather marginal hoped-for profits sufficiently attractive to get the industrial program started and because the plutonium is used for bombs, the nuclear electric power program may be considered a handmaiden of the armaments program and its contribution to environmental pollution may be blamed partly on the arms race.

Most of the radioactivity produced by a reactor stays inside the metal fuel elements in the reactor core. After a period of a year or two the reactor is shut down while the fuel is removed and replaced. The partially spent fuel is sent to a reprocessing plant where the radioactive wastes are extracted in acid solution that is kept so hot by the radioactive decay that it boils if it is not continually cooled. This extremely lethal brew must be prevented from entering the environment, but the containment is not perfect despite all the care taken.

At present, such high-level wastes in this country are stored in about 200 large underground steel-and-concrete tanks, holding as much as a million gallons each. Most of these wastes came from weapons production not associated with electric power production. The radioactive intensity of the liquid (measured in a unit known as a "curie") may run as high as a thousand curies per gallon or more. This is so lethal that if only three gallons were distributed equally among the entire world's population, this would suffice to reach in everyone on earth what is considered the danger point in radiation for the human body. Yet we already have in those buried tanks a hundred million gallons of the stuff, and apparently plan to go on producing it at an ever-increasing rate. These storage tanks require most elaborate perpetual care. They not only need power to cool them, but new high-quality tanks must be installed about every twenty years, on through the centuries, to replace old tanks damaged by radiation. Already failure of one tank has spilled 60,000 gallons of that lethal brew to find its uncertain way through the soil.

During the routine operation of reactors and fuel-processing plants there are also both planned and in-advertent releases of low-level wastes that contaminate air and water. The hot fuel elements in a reactor are sealed in a thin metal bonding intended to prevent the cooling fluid from coming into direct contact with the uranium and absorbing the radioactive fission products. However, in the power-generating plants, technology is pushed to its limit of high temperature and the metal seal frequently fails. It would be too expensive to inter-rupt operation for each failure, so leaks are tolerated in something like one per cent of the fuel elements be-fore shutdown. This is one route by which strontium and other radioactive fission products get into rivers.

Krypton 85 is a radioactive gas which, like neon and argon, does not easily react with other atoms to form solids, and remains a gas that escapes into the atmos-phere. Some of it goes up the stack at the reactor, be-cause of leaks, and the rest of it escapes at the fuel-processing plant. When breathed in air, a little of it dissolves in body fats. Radioactive tritium, the stuff of the H-bomb, is also produced in reactors and finds its way both into the atmosphere and into water supplies. It enters into bodily processes as part of water molecules.

The annual amount of the release of hazardous ele-ments from any nuclear plant is limited by standards set up by the Atomic Energy Commission. Since it is impossible to pinpoint all radioactive damage at low levels, the standards necessarily depend on somewhat arbitrary judgments. At high levels, it is known how much radiation will probably kill a man, and how much will probably give him serious radiation sickness. Permissible doses for workers in ,atomic plants are set well below that level, about one per cent of the lethal standard per year. But for the general populace, the permissible level is set about ten times lower, partly because of the possible seriousness of genetic damage.

Thus, the "maximum permissible dose" for the public is far below the level of identifiably radioactive damage to the individual and may seem to be a conservative standard. The guideline figure for the permitted level of radiation exposure for the general public as a result of reactor operation is set at such a level that if the whole population of the United States were to receive this additional exposure continuously, data now available on cancer incidence show that it would result in more than ten thousand deaths annually. While this number is small compared with the population, it is a large number of people to kill with a deliberate change in the environment. The radiation specialists who arrived at this conclusion, J. W. Gofman and A. R. Tamplin of Berkeley and Livermore, California, advocate that the permitted limit be reduced tenfold. Such a reduction, if enforced, would drastically modify the operation of commercial reactors.

The release from the stack of a single atomic plant is limited, so that it may not exceed the permitted level for people in the neighborhood, on a yearly average. If it does exceed the permitted level for a short time in an accidental release, as sometimes happens, the power level must be reduced the rest of the year to compensate. But a combination of a temperature inversion to keep the gases close to the ground, wind direction, and an accidental release can give some people a dose far above the "maximum permissible." As nuclear power plants become more numerous, the release from many plants may compound the exposure to radiation for persons in a wider area.

The commercial fuel processing plant at West Valley, New York, is responsible for keeping its low-level waste within permissible limits after discharge into a creek. It remained for University of Rochester scientists, acting on their own initiative as environment buffs, to discover that the radioactivity of the creek was far above the maximum permissible limit. Such considerations have led to clamor for an effective independent agency to set and enforce the safety standards, since AEC is now both promoter of nuclear power and its own policeman.

Radiation does its damage to individual cells within the body, and there is good reason to believe that genes and the rapidly multiplying cells in unborn and young children are more sensitive to such damage than are the cells in adults. Study of survivors of Hiroshima showed little genetic damage, but there the bomb burst high in the air and its debris was carried away in the mushroom cloud. More recent studies on mice have shown that strontium 90, which is spread from bomb debris and reactors, has a special affinity for causing genetic damage leading to fetal and infant mortality, in addition to its tendency to settle in bone and cause cancer and leukemia more in the young than in adults. It thus appears that radiation-induced fetal and infant mortality may pose a more serious problem than cancer in adults.

As the arms race goes on piling overkill on overkill, an all-out nuclear war could cause fallout extremely more intense than that caused by testing in the late 1950s and early 1960s. If testing caused fetal and infant deaths at the rate of something like one per 100 births, as Dr. E. J. Sternglass of the University of Pittsburgh claims, then a nuclear war causing 100 times as much fallout could presumably kill approximately all children born, and thus end the human race. From the way heavier doses affect adults, it could be surmised that considerably less than 100 times the test-era fallout might eliminate the next generation.

Even though we take the view that the Sternglass

Corporations and Pollution

by RALPH NADER

THE MODERN corporation's structure, impact, and public accountability are the central issues in any program designed to curb or forestall the contamination of air, water, and soil by industrial activity. While there are other sources of pollution, such as municipalities dumping untreated or inadequately treated sewage, industrial processes and products are the chief contributors to the long-term destruction of natural resources that each year increases the risks to human health and safety.

Moreover, through active corporate citizenship, industry could soon overcome many of the obstacles in the way of curbing non-corporate pollution. The mighty automobile industry, centered around and in Detroit, never thought it part of its role to press the city of

RALPH NADER *is the outspoken public advocate who came into national prominence four years ago with his book,* Unsafe at Any Speed. *This spring, reports of "Nader's Raiders" on pesticides and on air and water pollution will be published.*

Detroit to construct a modern sewage treatment plant. The automobile moguls, whose products, according to Department of Health, Education and Welfare data, account for fifty-five to sixty per cent of the nation's air pollution, remained silent as the city's obsolete and inadequate sewage facilities dumped the wastes of millions into the Detroit River. Obviously, local boosterism does not include such elementary acts of corporate citizenship.

The toilet training of industry to keep it from further rupturing the ecosystem requires an overhaul of the internal and external levers which control corporations. There are eight areas in which policies must be 'changed to create the pressures needed to make corporate entities and the people who run them cease their destruction of the environment:

ONE—The conventional way of giving the public a share in private decisions that involve health and safety hazards is to establish mandatory standards through a public agency. But pollution control standards set by governmental agencies can fall far short of their purported objectives unless they are adequately drafted, kept up to date, vigorously enforced, and supported by sanctions when violated. Behind the adoption of such standards, there is a long administrative process, tied to a political infrastructure. The scientific-engineering-legal community has a key independent role to play in this vital and complex administrative-political process. Almost invariably, however, its talents have been retained on behalf of those to be regulated. Whether in Washington or in state capitals around the country, the experts demonstrate greater loyalty to their employers than to their professional commitments in the public interest.

This has been the regular practice of specialists testifying in behalf of coal and uranium mining companies on the latters' environmental contamination in Appalachia and the Rocky Mountain regions. Perhaps the most egregious example of willing corporate servility was a paper entitled "We've Done the Job—What's Next?" delivered by Charles M. Heinen, Chrysler's vehicle emissions specialist, at a meeting of the Society of Automotive Engineers last spring.

Heinen, whose paper bordered on technical pornography, said the auto industry had solved the vehicle pollution problem with an eighty per cent reduction of hydrocarbons and a seventy per cent reduction of carbon monoxide between the 1960 and 1970 model years. He avoided mentioning at least four other vehicle pollutants—nitrogen oxides, lead, asbestos, and rubber tire pollutants. He also failed to point out that the emissions control performance of new cars degrades after a few thousand miles, and that even when new they do not perform under traffic conditions as they do when finely tuned at a company test facility. The overall aggregate pollution from ever greater numbers of vehicles in more congested traffic patterns also escaped Heinen's company-indentured perceptions.

Two—Sanctions against polluters are feeble and out of date, and, in any case, are rarely invoked. For example, the Federal air quality act has no criminal penalties no matter how willful and enduring the violations. In New Jersey, New York, and Illinois, a seventy-one year old Federal anti-water pollution law was violated with total impunity by industry until the Justice Department moved against a few of the violators in recent months. Other violators in other states are yet to be subjected to the law's enforcement. To be effective, sanctions should come in various forms, such as non-reimbursable fines, suspensions, dechartering of corporations, required disclosure of violations in company promotional materials, and more severe criminal penalties. Sanctions, consequently, should be tailored to the seriousness and duration of the violation.

It is expressive of the anemic and nondeterrent quality of existing sanctions that offshore oil leaks contaminating beaches for months, as in Santa Barbara, brought no penalty to any official of any offending company. The major controversy in Santa Barbara was whether the company—Union Oil—or the Government or the residents would bear the costs of cleaning up the mess. And even if the company bore the costs initially, the tax laws would permit a considerable shifting of this cost onto the general taxpayer.

THREE—The existing requirements for disclosure of the extent of corporate pollution are weak and flagrantly flouted. The Federal Water Pollution Control Administration (FWPCA) has been blocked since 1963 by industrial polluters (working with the Federal Bureau of the Budget) from obtaining information from these companies concerning the extent and location of discharges of pollutants into the nation's waterways. For three years, the National Industrial Waste Inventory has been held up by the Budget Bureau and its industry "advisers," who have a decisive policy role. Led by the steel, paper, and petroleum industries, corporate polluters have prevented the FWPCA from collecting specific information on what each company is putting into the water. Such information is of crucial importance to the effective administration of the water pollution law and the allocation of legal responsibility for violations.

Counties in California have been concealing from their citizens the identity of polluters and the amounts of pollution, using such weak, incredible arguments to support their cover-up as the companies' fear of revealing "trade secrets." California state agencies have refused to disclose pesticide application data to representatives of orchard workers being gradually poisoned by the chemicals. Once again the trade secret rationale was employed.

The real reason for secrecy is that disclosure of such information would raise public questions about why government agencies have not been doing their jobs—and would facilitate legal action by injured persons against the polluters. What must be made clear to both corporate and public officials is that no one has the right to a trade secret in lethality.

Massive and meticulous "fish bowl" disclosure requirements are imperative if citizens are to be alerted, at the earliest possible moment, to the flow of silent violence assaulting their health and safety, and that of unborn generations as well. This disclosure pattern, once established, must not lapse into a conspiracy between private and public officials, a conspiracy of silence against citizens and the public interest. A good place to start with such company-by-company disclosure is in the corporation's annual report, which now reveals only financial profits or losses; it should also reveal the social costs of pollution by composition and tonnage.

FOUR—Corporate investment in research and development of pollution controls is no longer a luxury to be left to the decision or initiative of a few company officers. Rather, such research and development must be required by law to include reinvestment of profits, the amount depending on the volume of pollution inflicted on the public. For example, in 1969 General Motors grossed $24 billion, yet last year spent less than $15 million on vehicle and plant pollution research and development, although its products and plants contribute some thirty-five per cent of the nation's air pollution by tonnage. A formula proportional to the size of a company and its pollution could be devised as law, with required periodic reporting of the progress of the company's research and its uses. A parallel governmental research and development program aimed at developing pollution-free product prototypes suitable for mass production, and a Federal procurement policy favoring the purchase of less-polluting products, are essential external impacts.

FIVE—Attention must be paid to the internal climate

for free expression and due process within the corporate structure. Again and again, the internal discipline of the corporate autocracy represses the civic and professional spirit of employees who have every right to speak out or blow the whistle on their company after they have tried in vain, working from the inside, to bring about changes that will end pollution practices. Professional employees—scientists, engineers, physicians—have fewer due process safeguards than the blue collar workers in the same company protected by their union contract.

When Edward Gregory, a Fisher Body plant inspector for General Motors in St. Louis, publicly spoke out in 1966 on inadequate welding that exposed Chevrolet passengers to exhaust leakage, the company ignored him for a few years, but eventually recalled more than two million cars for correction. GM knew better than to fire Gregory, a member of the United Auto Workers.

In contrast, scientists and engineers employed by corporations privately tell me of their reluctance to speak out—within their companies or outside them—about hazardous products. This explains why the technical elites are rarely in the vanguard of public concern over corporate contamination. Demotion, ostracism, dismissal are some of the corporate sanctions against which there is little or no recourse by the professional employee. A new corporate constitutionalism is needed, guaranteeing employees' due process rights against arbitrary reprisals, but its precise forms require the collection of data and extensive study. Here is a major challenge to which college faculty and students can respond on the campus and in field work.

SIX—The corporate shareholder can act, as he rarely does, as a prod and lever for jolting corporate leaders out of their lethargy. The law and the lawyers have rigged the legal system to muffle the voice of shareholders, particularly those concerned with the broader social costs of corporate enterprise. However, for socially conscious and determined stockholders there are many functions that can be performed to help protect the public (including themselves) from industrial pollution.

Shareholders must learn to take full advantage of such corporate practices as cumulative voting, which permits the "single-shot" casting of all of a shareholder's ballots for one member of the board of directors. Delegations of stockholders can give visibility to the issues by lobbying against their company's ill-advised policies in many forums apart from the annual meeting—legislative hearings, agency proceedings, town meetings, and the news media, for example. These delegations will be in a position to expose company officers to public judgment, something from which executives now seem so insulated in their daily corporate activities.

SEVEN—Natural, though perhaps unexercised, countervailing forces in the private sector can be highly influential incentives for change. For example, the United Auto Workers have announced that pollution will be an issue in the collective bargaining process with automobile company management this year; the union hopes to secure for workers the right not to work in polluting activities, or in a polluted environment. Insurance companies could become advocates for loss prevention in the environmental field when confronted with policyholder, shareholder, and citizen demonstrative action. Through their political influence, their rating function in evaluating risks and setting premium charges, and their research and development capability, insurance companies could exert a key countervailing stress on polluters. Whether they do or not will first depend on citizen groups to whip them into action.

EIGHT—Environmental lawsuits, long blocked by a conservative judiciary and an inflexible judicial system, now seem to be coming into their own—a classic example of how heightened public expectations, demands, and the availability of facts shape broader applications of ancient legal principles. Environmental pollution is environmental violence—to human beings and to property. The common law has long recognized such violence against the person as actionable or enjoinable. What has been lacking is sufficient evidence of harm and avoidability to persuade judges that such hitherto invisible long-range harm outweighed the economic benefits of the particular plant activity in the community.

It now appears that such lawsuits will gain greater acceptance, especially as more evidence and more willing lawyers combine to breathe contemporary reality into long-standing legal principles. An amendment to the U.S. Constitution providing citizens with basic rights to a clean environment has been proposed; similar amendments to state constitutions are being offered. Such generic provisions can only further the judicial acceptance of environmental lawsuits. Imaginative and bold legal advocacy is needed here. The *forced consumption* of industrial pollutants by 200 million Americans must lead to a recognition of legal rights in environmental control such as that which developed with civil rights for racial minorities over the last two decades.

Three additional points deserve the attention of concerned citizens:

First, a major corporate strategy in combating antipollution measures is to engage workers on the company side by leading them to believe that such measures would threaten their livelihood. This kind of industrial extortion in a community—especially a company town —has worked before and will again unless citizens anticipate and confront it squarely.

Second, both industry spokesmen and their governmental allies (such as the President's Science Adviser, Lee DuBridge) insist that consumers will have to pay the price of pollution control. While this point of view may be an unintended manifestation of the economy's administered price structure, it cannot go unchallenged. Pollution control must not become another lever to lift up excess profits and fuel the fires of inflation. The costs of pollution control technology should come from corporate profits which have been enhanced by the use of the public's environment as industry's private sewer. The sooner industry realizes that it must bear the costs of cleanups, the more likely it will be to employ the quickest and most efficient techniques.

Finally, those who believe deeply in a humane ecology must act in accordance with their beliefs. They must so order their consumption and disposal habits that they can, in good conscience, preach what they actually practice. In brief, they must exercise a personal discipline as they advocate the discipline of governments and corporations.

The battle of the environmentalists is to preserve the physiological integrity of people by preserving the natural integrity of land, air, and water. The planet earth is a seamless structure with a thin slice of sustaining air, water, and soil that supports almost four billion people. This thin slice belongs to all of us, and we use it and hold it in trust for future earthlings. Here we must take our stand.

No Second Chance for Man

by KENNETH E. BOULDING

ONE OF THE agreeable things about the young of any generation is that they tend to think that they invented the world, and it is this indeed that keeps the world fresh. It is likewise a strong sign of being over sixty that one points out, much to the distress of the young, that a great deal of what is happening has happened before. The current excitement about the environment in particular is at least the third peak of interest in this particular issue in this century.

KENNETH E. BOULDING *is professor of economics and director of social and economic research for the Institute of Behavioral Science at the University of Colorado. Among his many books are* The Image *and* The Meaning of the Twentieth Century. *Two new books will soon be published:* Economics as a Science *and* A Primer of Social Dynamics.

Excitement about the environment seems to have a generation cycle of some thirty years. The first major peak in this country was at the turn of the century, associated particularly with Governor Gifford Pinchot, America's first professional forester, Theodore Roosevelt, and the first conservation movement, which gave us the Bureau of Reclamation and expanded the National Park and Forest System. The second peak was in the 1930s, with the dust bowl and the great dust storm of 1934, in which noticeable portions of the Great Plains landed on the steps of the Capitol in Washington, and this produced the Soil Conservation Act, contour plowing, and all that.

It is not wholly surprising, therefore, that another generation has discovered that the world is not wholly indestructible. Now it is perhaps air rather than soil, and cities rather than forests, which have created the anxiety, but the anxiety is of course quite legitimate. There is nothing in the proposition that something has happened before to argue against its happening now. It is possible, however, to get a certain perspective on what is happening now, and perhaps also to avoid certain mistakes, if we see it as part of the much larger process.

We probably know more about the economics of the environment, surprisingly enough, than about its biology and physics. One of the real problems of the present crisis is that we know so little about the earth as a total physical system, particularly in regard to the atmosphere and the hydrosphere, and even less perhaps about the totality of the biosphere. Consequently, it is easy to develop scares about the oceans and the atmosphere which may have some validity but which are extremely hard to evaluate in the absence of an adequate earth science.

The science of the total earth is still undeveloped, and the earth sciences for the most part have been "micro" rather than "macro" in their interests. It is not surprising that we know much more about Walden

Pond than we do about the oceans, or about the inside of a chimney than we do about the atmosphere, simply because at the macro level there is a great deal more to know. As far as I can judge from the gossip I hear, meteorologists are still quite uncertain as to whether the earth is cooling down or warming up as a result of man's activities, and one feels that even economists have a better idea than that as to whether we are in some sense going up or down.

The economics of the environment has two aspects— a short-run and a long-run. Within the short-run, with a horizon, shall we say, of another generation, there are two further aspects, one involving the relative price structure and the other involving distribution of income and wealth. A great many short-run environmental problems arise because of a defect in the relative price system in that not enough negative commodities have negative prices. A negative commodity is a "bad," as opposed to a "good." It is something which diminishes utility rather than increases it.

Virtually all processes of production produce a whole set of joint products, some of which are "goods" and some of which are "bads." The bads may be physical products, like water and air pollution; they may be more subtle things like noise pollution; or they may be still more subtle, like information pollution—the spreading of misinformation—which is perhaps the most important pollution problem of all. The pollution of the information system by lies, propaganda, and other communications which increase ignorance and malevolence is probably much more threatening to the future of mankind at the moment than is the pollution of water and air, although it is much harder to deal with.

Market institutions tend to be ineffective in the pricing of bads, mainly because the system of property does not encompass them sufficiently. The legal system tries to do this in the law of torts, under which a private person can sue for damages. These damages (bads) then become, as it were, a form of property for which one can be legally compensated. A great many bads, however, are nobody's property, and the legal system, as at present constituted, is therefore inadequate to deal with them.

Just as "public goods" constitute a special category which requires a political rather than a market form of organization, similarly "public bads" require political organization and action if they are to be dealt with. The simplest and most obvious way to deal with them is through a tax system, and a system of graduated effluent taxes is certainly the place to begin in the control of pollution, even though it is not a panacea or a universally practicable device. It is applicable mainly to industrial pollution, but it is hard to apply to what might be called household or individual pollution, the sort of thing that is represented by the personal automobile, simply because the individual pollutant is in such small quantities that it is hard to identify.

We have a rather similar problem in information pollution. We have a law of slander for what we might call private information pollution, but this is not adequate to deal with the problem of public information pollution, which requires, indeed, a development of constitutionality beyond what we now have.

The real question here is whether the sense of public concern is strong enough to persuade people to sacrifice certain private goods for the suppression of public bads. This is an example of the famous "freeloading" problem. The individual interest is to go on polluting as long as the rest of society picks up the tab. It requires, therefore, a sense of political awareness and a political community before this problem can be solved. One can predict with a good deal of confidence that the present excitement will not have much result unless it can be translated into political action. Unfortunately, there is a strong tendency for political action to provide mainly ritualistic and rhetorically satisfying solutions to problems, particularly when there is a real conflict of interests between the public and the private. The principle of "the public be damned" is the secret vice of practically everybody.

The problem is complicated by the fact that almost anything we do about the environment is likely to have considerable effect on the distribution of income and wealth. A good many of the problems that we visualize today arise because many things which used to be the privilege of only the rich have now moved a long way down the income scale to become the privilege of a large majority of the people.

Most of the pressures on the environment, whether in terms of air pollution, urban sprawl, super highways, artificial fertilizers and insecticides, and so on, arise because the mass of the people in the developed countries are no longer as poor as they used to be. Per capita real income in the United States has about doubled in the last thirty or forty years. There has not, however, been much in the way of the *relative* redistribution of income—that is, the proportion of the total income going to different income groups is remarkably constant. We have made the poor richer not by making the rich poorer, which is hardly ever a good recipe for this, but by increasing output. Increasing output, however, inevitably increases the strain on the environment. The most obvious, though not the most desirable, way to reduce pressure on the environment, therefore, is to stop the poor getting richer—that is, to redistribute income back towards the rich again.

There is some distressing evidence that this was one of the principal results of the first two great environmental agitations. In spite of the fact, for instance, that the Bureau of Reclamation probably represents the high water mark of socialist ideology in the United States, having been set up deliberately to undermine the monopoly of private capital, to lower interest rates, and to subsidize small farmers, its ultimate effect may well have been to subsidize rich farmers much more than poor ones.

This is even more true of the agricultural legislation which emerged out of the 1930s, which has been so successful in subsidizing the rich farmers that it created a fantastic technological upsurge in agriculture, and in so doing was the major factor in creating the current urban problem. I would not blame the Soil Conservation Service for all of this, but certainly it was part of a policy which has driven the poor farmer off the land into the cities, largely into the ghettos, and has created in the United States a hereditary aristocracy of super-peasants.

Even if we look at the public lands policy, we can see clearly, in the West especially, that National Parks and National Forests have mainly had the effect of keeping poor people out of the mountains. If it had

not been for the scarcity of private lands and the fact that the public lands benefited mainly the private owners who were adjacent, considerable numbers of the displaced poor might have moved into the Western mountains and turned them into another Appalachia. This certainly would not have been desirable in the long run, but it does mean that the public land policy imposed a hidden cost on the poor, for which they were not compensated.

These earlier conservationist policies can be defended, of course, both in terms of the preservation of the enjoyment of nature, in terms of the conservation of natural resources, and in terms of economic development itself. The brute fact, however, is that it is not the poor who enjoy the beauties of nature, or who are likely to benefit much from the conservation of natural resources; it is mainly the rich, who both create and gain the most from economic development. One can see the present environmental excitement tending along the same lines. We will solve the problem of the automobile by taxing it heavily so as to support electrically powered public transportation which would push us back to about 1900, when automobiles were the privilege of the rich and public transportation was the much less convenient privilege of the poor.

Behind the noble banner of pollution control and environmental preservation, which is supposed to bring us all together and unite us in a great war on generally agreed upon vice, there is an uncomfortable shadow, the claims of the poor. We see this even more dramatically on a world scale where it is the increasing population of the poor, and their increasing demands for development—the only thing which can give them increased per capita income—which is really threatening to create a major world environmental crisis. The environmental disasters that threaten the rich countries in the next thirty years are almost trivial compared with the environmental disasters that threaten the poor countries of the tropics. A part of this is the result of the undeveloped nature of science itself and of the technology which is based on it. Science on the whole is a temperate zone culture and science-based engineering even more so.

It is easy, therefore, to make disastrous mistakes when we go about developing the tropics, simply because of our ignorance of tropical ecosystems, and also because tropical systems, at least in many parts of the world, seem to be much more precarious than those in the temperate zone. Dam building in the tropics can be particularly disastrous. Diseases, such as schistosomiasis, evaporation, silt, erosion, and displaced peoples present problems on a scale unknown in the temperate zone. The ecological disaster with which Egypt is threatened by the Aswan Dam, and also by its uncontrollably expanding population, is on a much larger scale than anything that threatens in the entire temperate zone.

These environmental crises in the tropics, however, are arising precisely because the people in this part of the world are no longer content to live the way they have always done. Furthermore, the partial impact of science-based technology, particularly the introduction of public health measures, destroyed the old equilibrium forever. There seems to be no way back, fortunately, to a world in which the poor are quietly content to starve and allow the rich to govern them.

What all this means is that while short-run solutions to current environmental problems can probably be found fairly easily, the long-run problem is tough indeed, and will tax the intellectual and moral resources of mankind to the utmost. I have been describing this long-run problem as the problem of "re-entry into spaceship earth." Economic development has been compared not inaptly to a "takeoff." We are all aware that we are going through a period of enormous change and that the transition in the state of man which these few centuries represent is perhaps the greatest transition he has ever made or ever will have to make. We are now in the middle range of the voyage towards spaceship

earth, perhaps not yet at the middle, but it is not too soon to start thinking and preparing for the eventual slowdown of the increase in scientific knowledge, a slowdown in economic development, and a re-entry into a type of society which will probably be so different from anything in the past that we can hardly imagine it.

It is impossible to predict in any detail either the future of knowledge or of technology. One thing, however, is clear—that whatever the future society is like, it will have to inhabit a "spaceship earth," as Barbara Ward has called it, of highly limited resources, and it will have to develop a circular or "looped" material economy.

Up to the present period, man has lived psychologically, and to a large extent physically, on a "great plain," which has always had a horizon, always had a frontier, and he has always had somewhere else to go. His material economy, furthermore, has always been, with some possible exceptions, "linear," in the sense that it has gone from exhaustible resources of some kind, such as mines, wells, or even the stock of huntable animals, into dumps. Man's economic life even in the paleolithic period seems to have consisted of exhausting his environment and fouling his nest. As long as there was a new environment and a new nest to move into, this perhaps did not matter so much, and man, by reason of his remarkable learning capacity, was able to expand into the whole earth and become its dominant species.

The great phenomenon of the Twentieth Century, however, is closure. Even when I was a boy there were still unexplored places on the globe; today there are none. The space enterprise emphasizes as never before the smallness and the loneliness of planet earth. It is the only decent piece of real estate in an enormous volume of space. We are conscious also that the time we are living in is unique, that it will never be repeated again. There is no second chance for man. If he cannot succeed in organizing his little spaceship on a permanent, self-sustaining basis before he has exhausted the stock of geological capital on which his development now rests, he will never have another chance. He will be inhabiting a plundered planet with all its geological capital squandered.

It is clear, therefore, that spaceship earth will require a technology quite different from what we have now, one in which the atmosphere, the oceans, and the soil are virtually the only sources of man's material artifacts and in which as these artifacts are used up their material components are in effect returned to the sources from which they came. There seems nothing inherently impossible about a technology of this kind. Indeed, some of the Twentieth Century developments point towards it, such as the fixation of nitrogen from the air and the extraction of magnesium from the sea.

The great unknown is the energy requirement. We may be able to devise an economy without an increase of material entropy, that is, in which we do not on balance diffuse concentrated materials, but, thanks to the second law of thermodynamics (that closed systems run down), it is impossible to have any economy without an input of energy. Virtually the only outside input of energy into the earth comes from the sun and this will go on for a long time. We can supplement this by burning up the earth itself, either the fossil sunshine in the fossil fuels or the nuclear energy. If we solve the fission problem this, too, would go on for a long time, although we might be faced eventually with the inability to export enough energy into space. If we burn up too much of the earth, it may get too hot for us. We may eventually, therefore, be forced back on the input of solar energy and utilize this for the necessary material transformations.

What we do not know now within orders of magnitude is the total human population that a spaceship earth would support at a reasonable level. Perhaps this is something we do not need to know for a long time, but at some point it is going to be a crucial factor in human history. We might visualize an earth of self-contained households, each raising all its food in sewage-fed artificial-algae tanks on one half of the roof-top and capturing all its energy on the other half of the rooftop with a solar trap, using virtually indestructible equipment, clothing, and furniture, with transportation mainly in the form of information carried by

radiant energy. In this case I suppose we could have a world city with 100 billion people and a kind of universal Los Angelization. On the other hand, this may not be feasible and a much more elaborate structure may be necessary to support a considerably smaller population.

It seems absolutely impossible to predict what kind of social organization spaceship earth would require. One can visualize everything from a super-hierarchical Brave New World, with a small elite and a large number of happy robots, or one could visualize a highly decentralized society relying on automatic cybernetic controls in a virtually anarchic utopia.

What is clear in the midst of all this uncertainty is that in the light of the enormous intellectual and moral task which lies ahead of mankind, the political revolutions of the last 200 years fade into relative insignificance. Neither the American, the French, nor the Russian revolutions created fundamental changes in the state of man and the ideologies which supported them are quite inadequate to bear the weight of this enormous transition which man faces.

This is not to deny the importance of the political task. Indeed, the organization of the political life of the planet may well be the factor that will make the difference between successful re-entry and possibly quite irretrievable disaster, for a landing is more dangerous than a takeoff. The political task, however, and the intellectual labor which must precede it still largely lie ahead of us. This is an age of disillusionment with all previous political solutions and political organizations. Neither capitalism nor Communism can solve the imminent danger involved in the international threat system. Nobody has solved the problem of how to develop the tropics without either demographic or ecological disaster. Nobody has solved the problem of how to prevent the insidious corruption both of the culture of the powerful and the culture of the impotent. We need a new image of the total dynamics of the social system more realistic than those provided by ideologies either of the right or of the left.

If the present excitement about the environment is to produce more than emotion, platitudes, and attempts to take us back to the good old days when the poor knew their place, it will have to stimulate us to an analysis of social dynamics both more realistic and more appealing than any we now possess.

MEMO

by HENRY GIBSON

CUYAHOGA FILMS
Office of the President

FROM: OO

TO: J VanG Jr.

DATE: 4/15/70

DEAR JAMIE:

How proud your Dad must be to make his first official act as our new studio Board Chairman the sub-

---

HENRY GIBSON *is both actor and poet. In addition to starring in the "Laugh-In" television show, he was unofficial adviser to the Environmental Teach-In, unofficial spokesman for Keep America Beautiful, and unofficial crusader for the preservation of our natural resources. His recently published book,* A Flower Child's Garden of Verses, *will soon be followed by a collection of ecological poems.*

---

mission of your fabulous script for a futuristic anti-pollution musical. And, believe me, I'm tickled pink with it. I never really thought anybody could cover the entire subject in only 1,700 pages. Do you major in Biology?

There's no question the subject is hot right now. But how long will it *stay* hot? If the boys here are kind of divided, it's only because they remember how fast Haight-Ashbury fizzled out. I'm all for the project, of course, but *they* say we would of had to start a pollution musical three years ago for our release date to coincide with all those cover stories in *Newsweek, Life,* and *Time.* I mean, look at the hula hoop and Batman. You got to move fast today. Also, they say stories like this don't usually work if you focus on more than one "heavy."

Still, we're going to make the picture, so I don't want to be too negative as you've sure got a lot of ideas for a nineteen-year-old kid who's never written a screen-play before, let alone been inside a studio.

I personally think your script is a beaut impact-wise —especially that "end of the world" scene where you cut from the alarm on the population-explosion machine to the polar ice cap melting and then zoom in on the drowning Statue of Liberty.

However, the following are some notes, suggestions, questions about where you go after that:

1. Isn't the parallel between the Santa Barbara oil well blowout in January '69 and Pearl Harbor a little heavy? I mean, "December Seventh" is kind of a catchy date that fits the picture—but "January Twenty-eighth" sounds real clumsy to *say,* if you follow me. It's just not an image-making date. Anyway you're better off being positive. Like when you say "Support Your Local Tree." Now that's the kind of slogan you pay good money for!

2. I'm not too sure about the part where modern art

murals get painted by soot from factory chimneys. But it may get a laugh if we score it with *Smoke Gets In Your Eyes*.

3. I really flipped over Huntley-Brinkley giving the Dow Jones Environmental Averages—you know, "garbage steady, population up . . . " etc. But we ran a twelve-month check on the thirty-city Nielsens and think we should keep Cronkite on standby, just in case they drop. (Incidentally, I *don't* buy your commercial for lead-free gasoline. Saying: "It may take longer to get there but at least you can open the window" is just plain smartass.)

4. Talked to the Art Department about building the giant X-Ray Machine that shows all the asbestos in your lungs, the DDT in your tissues, the Strontium 90 in your bones, etc. They feel it's so expensive we should maybe just settle for a Miss Pollution Beauty Parade instead. How does that grab you?

5. Same goes for the Giant Chess Game pitting sixteen kids against the monsters of Pesticide, Oilslick, Nuclear Waste, etc. I for one love the idea that "capture" means "death," especially when you angle up on those cropdusting planes—but who are we to argue with the budget boys?

6. The connection between missile defense and pollution defense escapes me. Are you trying to suggest an anti-pollution missile? If so, I'm afraid Dr. Strangelove has already gone that route.

7. The meeting where WIDESPAN members draft a Declaration of Interdependence might make it if you didn't go into that long song and dance about WIDESPAN standing for Wilderness Society-Izaac Walton League-Defenders of Wildlife-Environmental Defense Fund-Sierra Club-Population Crisis Committee-Audubon Society-National Wildlife Federation. Why not just let it stand for WIDESPAN?

8. I refuse to even discuss the business of the "haloed" automobile on a pedestal surrounded by a crowd of

kneeling worshippers. First, it's unlikely. Second, I don't find such things amusing. And, third, we need a family rating.

9. Ditto the overcrowding scene where homeless mobs break into the Vatican for breathing-space. I mean, if they wouldn't do it at the White House, why would they do it there? Maybe we could reset this someplace in South America.

10. Sorry, but I just don't believe the kid when he tells his parents he's going off to join the Earth Corps.

11. About your Supreme Court scene where mankind is on trial—I guess it's OK to make Justices out of Nelson, Nader, and Commoner, but who ever heard of names like Blatnik, Odum, and Yannecone? (Is he the guy from Newark?) If we're going to use real-life conservationists, I think we should stick to known quantities like Charles A. Lindbergh and Arthur Godfrey. Names you can trust. (Also, shouldn't one of them be black?)

12. It's when you show things getting better that the script really starts to drag.

13. Nobody cares how the Smithsonian's super-data machine finally coordinates all those environmental research projects—unless maybe you get a broad like Julie Newmar to play the part of the machine, but they already did that on TV.

14. What the hell kind of a name is Joseph Wood Krotch? Remember, we need a family rating.

Well, Jamie, this about covers my reactions, and now that you know we see eye-to-eye I'm sure we'll end up with the kind of product that has made Cuyahoga famous.

My best to your Mom and Dad.

Love,
(UNCLE) OLLIE

cc: J VanG Sr.

Spring, and a Time to Listen

by HAL BORLAND

THERE'S SOMETHING about the vernal equinox that takes me right back to fundamentals. It reminds me, for one thing, that the year began with March, not January, before the Roman emperors began tinkering with the calendar. It makes me thankful that winter doesn't last six months instead of three. It reminds me

---

HAL BORLAND, *conservationist, essayist, and novelist, is probably best known for his distinguished nature writing. He grew up in Colorado and now lives on a Connecticut farm in the lower Berkshires. His many books include* Homeland: A Report from the Country, *a collection of twenty of his essays in* The Progressive, *1964-1968. He edited* Our Natural World, *a selection of writings on American land and wildlife. His new book,* Country Editor's Boy, *will be published this spring.*

---

that April is at hand—April, a teen-age girl with a bunch of daffodils in her hand, stars in her eyes, a taunt in her laughter, and an inclination to play practical jokes. And the equinox makes me glad I live where I do. Doubly glad this year.

Up here in the hills we know that we always have to earn spring by enduring January and February and sometimes March. This year, by the middle of February we began to think the price had been inflated a good deal more than the six per cent they concede for everything else. We had the snowiest December and the coldest January on record. Groundhog Day was dour and lowery, as usual, and spring didn't come early, also as usual. However, here is April, bought and paid for. April, with blue sky, an early thunderstorm, a late snowstorm, cursed with March's leftovers, blessed with a foretaste of May. April, yellow rocket and shadblow and dandelions, pink buds on the apple trees, purple leaves on the lilacs, peepers in the twilight, robins in the dawn.

And high time. It's much easier to listen to and believe the facts of conservation in April than in January, and the tide of environmental concern has been rising all winter. For years a handful of us have been warning that things were getting out of hand, but we were largely talking to a vacuum. The technologists, the industrial chemists, the public officials, and most of the general public, when they heard us at all, said, "Nonsense! Who cares about a little smog and smoke? They are signs of full employment. What does a little sewage and industrial waste matter in the rivers and lakes? Water is water, isn't it? And what if the miracle pesticides do kill a few songbirds? We are prosperous, the most prosperous nation in the world, with the highest standard of living in history. That's what really matters."

But finally even they began to choke on their own fumes and gag on their own water. And conservation became a popular cause.

A few weeks ago my friend John and I went to Hartford to attend a meeting of the Governor's committee to develop an environmental policy for Connecticut. John taught English in an Ivy League college for some years, then quit and came up here and became a dairy farmer to get back to reality. "Isn't it ironic," John said as we were driving to Hartford that day, "that we destroy so many comfortable, satisfying things in our environment before we decide it's time to develop a policy to save that environment?" And from that question we went on to discuss the comfortable, satisfying things in life the way we try to live it, the things any sensible policy would try to preserve.

There are the three fundamentals, of course—the land, the air, the water. Curb their pollution and we will all live much healthier lives. Our committee, we knew, was going to try to work out a program to do just that, clean up the land, the air, the water, improve the environment. But there were factors beyond those obvious ones which were almost impossible to codify and, as we said after discusssing the matter for ten minutes, those were the factors that make the life we live, as countrymen, worth while.

We didn't even try to discuss those factors. We named a few of them, but that was all. The sense of belonging to the land. The look of a pasture after a snowfall. Birch trees in first leaf. The cool air that flows down from a mountainside at dusk on a summer evening. Autumn in New England. The taste of spring water. A deer in the home pasture at dawn. A catbird singing in a lilac bush. The smell of fresh-cut hay in June. The smell of a newly plowed field in April. A whippoorwill calling from 3 a.m. till 3:45, without one real pause for breath. The taste of wild grape jelly.

It sounds ridiculous, in a way, I suppose, unless you have experienced all those things and know what they mean. Of what possible importance can things like that be in a conservation program or an environmental policy? Well, the best answer I can come up with offhand is that without such things life as we know it would be not merely stagnant but sterile. An environment is more than the air you breathe, the water you drink, and the people around you. It is the land around you, and the wind and rain and trees and grass, the sun, moon, and stars. It is all those things and the subtleties inherent which go into your thinking and your dreams, or lack of them.

As I say, John and I didn't discuss such matters. We merely named a few of them that seemed important in a very personal way. But I intend to discuss and try to explain those matters here, or at least a few of them, so that when we are tempted to immerse ourselves in air and water and soil we can perhaps be aware, at least, of some of these intangibles.

I am sure there are plenty of other writers and talkers to expatiate on the need for open space, breathing room, grass, trees, potable water, breathable air, and the lethal nature of biocides. Others undoubtedly will discuss our incredible mountains of trash and garbage, our billions of tons and gallons of industrial waste, our mad population growth.

But beyond the scientific fact that a tree is the best source of oxygen on earth is the fact that a tree is a tree. Not board feet of lumber, or gallons of turpentine, or rolls of newsprint. But a tree, a growing plant, a marvel of fiber and sap and bud and leaf and blossom. Shade in summer, and shelter for nesting birds. Nuts in autumn for hungry squirrels. And a beauty forever, with its haze of new leaves in the spring; its mass of green, fluttering in the breeze, pattering in the rain, casting shade, making life more pleasant in the summer; its color in the autumn, sheer beauty that not even the most enterprising chemist has yet been able to sell as a pigment or a flavor or a food. A tree, one of the most beautiful things on earth.

The land, of course, is a commodity. It is a building site, a field for corn or hay, a sand and gravel pit, a place to put a superhighway, or an airport, or a parking field. It is open space between houses, between towns. It is room for cities and suburbs to expand. But the land is also the only place where the fundamental green of the leaf grows. And that green is the fundamental sustenance of life. It manufactures the oxygen and it is the ultimate food of all of us, ant to elephant, horse to human being. That is the land. And when we want to have a piece of that land to stand on, to walk upon, to know intimately, it is more than mere acquisitiveness. It is fundamental with us, for we need to know and be in daily contact with the earth of our own origins. It's as simple as that. And we want some of the wild places preserved wild because that is where we can come close to the truth of life and the earth itself. We smell it when we plow a field in spring. We see it when we cut and cure hay in June. We taste it when we take in the garden crop in September. But we feel it, we are a part of it, when we go to a wilderness area at any time of the year.

Be practical and point out that every one of our songbirds and even our game birds is a partner of the farmer who is producing food for the millions. Nobody has yet invented a better insecticide than the birds in our dooryard. That is a basic reason the outcry was first made against DDT and its chemical kindred—it killed birds as well as insects. Later we found that it was far more harmful than that, but when we first pointed to the bird kill the chemical people scoffed at "the loss of a few songbirds." And they missed the whole point—missed it twice, in fact. First, a bird killed by DDT was only a symptom of far greater damage being done. Second, a songbird is more than a few ounces of flesh and feathers. It is song, for one thing. The birds were the first songsters on earth, and quite probably they taught man to sing. And it is beauty, of form and color and motion. It is that superb chorus which makes a summer dawn so memorable. It is the hummer at the petunias and the indigo bunting in the apple tree full of blossom, it is the scarlet tanager and the goldfinch and the cockaded cardinal. It is the catbird making sweet music and then making a travesty of his own song. It is, yes, the whippoorwill yelping interminably in the small hours of the night and you lying awake, counting. It is the eagle and the falcon and the soaring hawk.

Water is the most abundant element on earth, but clean water is becoming rare. Even clean ocean water has become scarce along the continental margins, thanks to the filthiest animal alive and his cities. Without water we all perish, of course. And it is fouled by every element of society and industry. What is a river? A

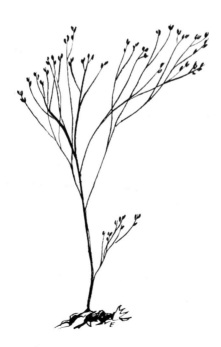

place to dump something you don't want or can't use. Just recently New York's Consolidated Edison atomic plant up the Hudson from New York City sucked fish into its cooling system through a defective screen. Conservationists complained of the fish kill, so Con Ed plugged the leaky screen and dumped 150,000 dead fish back into the river! Where else? The river was handy, and it would carry the dead fish away, to someone else's waterfront.

Water, to be used and abused. But also a majestic river, a beautiful, remote brook, a sweet mountainside spring. Give the countryman a good supply of sweet water and he can make a home anywhere. Give him a clean brook and he will fish for trout, a clean lake and he will catch bass for his supper. Water, the wet sweetness of this earth, the mountaintop cloud made tangible, the morning dew gathered into a stream. Water to refresh the air and the earth and all its creatures. Man is of that long line of red-blooded life which first appeared in the water. We are no longer aquatic, but from the time we stand in youthful wonder beside a spring brook till we sit in old age and watch the endless roll of the sea we feel a strong kinship with the waters of this earth. We marvel at the magnificence of a snowflake, a water crystal. We sleep content with the drone of rain on the roof. We slake our thirst, we cool our faces, we bathe our bodies with water. The blood that courses our veins is largely water. Small wonder the countryman cherishes his brooks and ponds and will fight to keep them and keep them clean.

Perhaps you begin to understand. More than air and water and soil are at stake. Conservation and environment are not so simple. There are ways of life, and there are fundamentals of living, that also need conserving, if only as reminders of what is possible for man if he ever again is master of his own life. Not as an example of the antique or the historical, not Grandfather's way, but a simpler way of life possible even today without privation or hardship or flight from reality.

What I am talking about is receptivity. Perhaps that sounds pretentious, but it really isn't. It is understanding and a willingness to participate. I have heard someone speak of "appreciation," but that is too precious a term; it smacks of the esthetic, and this is a thoroughly practical matter. Perhaps that is why I said at the start that April is a better time to discuss such matters than January. In April the world around you, particularly here in the country, cannot be ignored. You are receptive, or you are deaf, dumb, and blind, and an utter clod to boot. And I am not talking about the traveler out to see how many miles he can cover in a weekend, or about the bird watcher out to accumulate a longer list than her neighbor down the street. I am talking about understanding what is all around you, not merely counting or identifying.

We keep hearing that population is the ultimate cause of all these environmental problems, and in many areas that is true. Certainly some way should be found to make 1980, or 2000, less of a terminal deadline for human survival. Maybe disease will take care of that, or famine, or a cataclysmic war. But I have less fear of the standing-room-only prophecies than I have of the tendency to emulate the ants. And of the sophisticated disdain for all things rural, coupled with blind legislative insistence, largely of urban origin, that all farmland be vacated and all country folk be taken to the cities. You don't conserve anything that way, and you certainly don't improve environments. It often seems that the urban majority of our population, now up around eighty per cent I believe, is afraid of the open country except when passed through safely inside a speeding automobile or high above it in a supersonic transport. Afraid of open spaces and distrustful of their relatively few inhabitants.

Why? Not simple agoraphobia, I am sure. And not wholly a matter of thinking everyone living five miles from a metropolitan center is an oaf or a dolt. I think we all know now that a city lunkhead is just as witless as a rural simpleton, and the averages don't vary much per thousand. Can it be because they have forgotten so many things that should be remembered?

Actually, we all once lived close to the soil, even here in America. Well over half of us were still there within the memory of men barely old enough for Social Security. The ways of the country are in our blood, if not in our hearts, as a nation. We turn our back on them at our peril, and we embrace the technologies that have done so much to destroy our environment. We listened too long to the factory whistles, thinking that more was better, and bigger was best of all. Bigger cities, bigger industry, bigger armament, bigger wars.

And that is what this is all about, this sudden surge of concern over the environment. That's what some of us have been saying for twenty years or more. And now it's another April, another spring, and maybe it will be easier to listen to what was said all this time. As I said just a few paragraphs back, in April you are receptive, you listen and try to understand, or you are deaf, dumb, and blind, and an utter clod to boot. Let's stand on that for now. Let this be the time to separate the men from the clods.

Our Polluted Planet

by SENATOR GAYLORD A. NELSON

MAN LIVES on a limited, finite planet that spins in a mathematically precise orbit in the dead vacuum of space. The uniqueness of man's planet earth is that it is the only body in the solar system capable of supporting life.

Just how long it will be able to sustain life, however, is a question that is causing increasing concern to many scientists and ecologists. Our planet has only a thin veneer of soil that is supporting rapidly diminishing forests and a dwindling variety of animal species.

Senator Gaylord A. Nelson, *Wisconsin Democrat, was a leading spokesman for conservation and environmental protection long before the cause became fashionable. Now in his second Senate term, he has sponsored dozens of bills designed to combat pollution and to protect and expand the nation's natural resources. He was co-chairman with Representative Paul N. McCloskey, Jr., California Republican, of the National Teach-In on the Crisis of the Environment which was held on April 22, 1970.*

The scientists and ecologists have been warning for years that earth's resources are not endless and that soaring population growth and blind disregard for the most vital resources of air and water could bring disaster. They have stepped up their warnings of pending disaster, because they believe that the end is virtually imminent. Every major watershed in America has been polluted by the unbridled expansion of business and industry and by municipalities unwilling to clean their wastes adequately before dumping. Lake Erie, an important fresh water supply for millions of people, is almost dead, and most other major bodies of water in the nation are close behind.

Even the vast oceans, which make up three-fourths of the surface of the globe, face disaster and destruction. Man has looked to the oceans as the future source of food protein when the land becomes too crowded and too overworked to produce enough. But the pollution of the seas has become so serious that one noted ecologist has flatly predicted that the end of life in the seas could come in ten years.

Evidence of nature in rebellion has already been seen in the oceans, as mysterious events take place which scientists have under study. In the South Pacific, a marauding starfish is destroying coral reefs; without these barriers, many islands, including the Hawaiian, will lie unprotected from the pounding seas. Scientists are guessing that dredging, underwater blasting, overuse of lingering pesticides, or even radioactive fallout have killed the starfish's natural enemies.

Other events have been observed that have brought death to thousands of creatures living in and around the sea. Some were killed by the ugly oil spills off the coasts of California, the Gulf States, and Southern England. Some, however, remain unexplained—with only the dead fish, birds, clams, or crabs, tumbling by the thousands in the surf, indicating that something serious was wrong.

There is almost no way to escape the poisons of pollution. Day after day the thin envelope of air that surrounds the earth is mixed with the belching smoke and soot of tens of thousands of industrial smokestacks and incinerators and the deadly fumes from millions of automobiles, buses, and trucks exhausting gases and lead particles from fuel into the air. Just how long the atmosphere will be able to absorb these pollutants cannot be predicted accurately.

The environmental threats have begun to jolt many Americans from their indifference and disregard for the severely limited natural resources of man. A recent Gallup Poll conducted for the National Wildlife Federation revealed that fifty-one percent of all persons interviewed expressed "deep concern" about the effects of air pollution, water pollution, soil erosion, and the destruction of wildlife and natural resources. Most surprising was the fact that almost three out of every four of the persons interviewed said they would be willing to pay additional taxes to put a halt to these threats to life.

Even a limited survey of the ways in which man has been violating his environment demonstrates why the threat to life itself is so serious. The use of the deadly, long-lasting, poisonous pesticides is one of the most depressing examples. Each year, nearly one billion pounds of pesticides of all kinds are sprayed, dusted, fogged, or dumped in the United States—about five pounds for every man, woman, and child in the country.

The residues drift through the air, mingle with the waters to destroy aquatic life, and seep through the soil to contaminate the environment on a worldwide basis. Pesticide particles have been found, for example, in the tissues of reindeer in Alaska, in penguins in the Antarctic, and in the dust over the Indian Ocean. Several species of animal life, including the American bald eagle, the peregrine falcon, the osprey, and the Bermuda petrel are on the verge of extinction by pesticides.

A two-year national pesticide study completed by the

U.S. Bureau of Sport Fisheries and Wildlife found DDT in 584 of 590 samples of fish taken from forty-four rivers and lakes across the United States. The study revealed DDT residues ranging up to forty-five parts per million in the whole fish, a count more than *nine times higher* than the current Food and Drug Administration guideline level for DDT in fish.

The threat of pesticides to public health and safety was made shockingly obvious a year ago when the Food and Drug Administration seized 28,000 pounds of pesticide-contaminated Coho salmon in Lake Michigan. The concentration of DDT in the salmon was up to nineteen parts per million; the accumulation of dieldrin, a persistent and more toxic pesticide, up to 0.3 parts per million. Both levels are considered hazardous by the FDA and the World Health Organization.

Dangerous levels of DDT and other deadly pesticides have been found in tobacco and fruit, and vegetable producers constantly must take care to avoid having their crops banned from commercial markets.

An irony of the whole pesticide saga is that, time and again, the bugs have come out on top. Hit the insects with a pesticide, and a few hardy generations later, adaptation has developed a new breed that is immune to it. Rather than seeking the obvious answer of an alternative pest control, our response has usually been to use greater doses of the same old ineffective stuff.

Yet, despite the urgent warning by responsible scientists of imminent environmental disaster and health hazards from pesticides, Federal agencies have failed dismally to face the threatening problem. Not one agency has taken action that is bringing effective progress toward the goal of "eliminating" the use of persistent, toxic pesticides that was established six years ago by President Kennedy's Science Advisory Commission on Pesticides.

The appalling fact is that the Federal Government has been perpetuating this grave environmental and health problem rather than working to resolve it.

The Department of Agriculture has virtually ignored the hazards of pesticides, and Department spokesmen have opposed state action to ban DDT and have supported the pro-pesticide arguments of the chemical companies with scandalous devotion. In spite of the obvious need for alternatives to DDT and other hard pesticides, the Department has failed to launch an all-out research effort in this area. One spokesman for the Agricultural-Research Service admitted that the Department's program for improved means of nonchemical pest control is presently underfunded by at least $4 million.

It is obvious that the Department must research non-hazardous controls of pests and use its existing authority to place effective limitations on the use of all pesticides, including a complete cancellation of the registrations for the hard pesticides especially hazardous to the environment.

In the deepening national crisis facing our rivers and lakes, a dramatic new pollution source is developing— the massive discharges of heated water from nuclear power plants.

On Lake Michigan alone, seven nuclear power plants, several with capabilities larger than any in the history of power generation, are scheduled to be in operation by the mid-1970's. Together with the output around the lake of existing plants fueled by coal and oil, the higher volume of expelled heated water will raise the temperature of all of Lake Michigan by several degrees in the next few decades.

In addition to the threatened change in the taste and smell of drinking water near some of the plants, the delicate chain of Lake Michigan aquatic life, already severely threatened by other pollutants, could be further upset. Algae growth is already a problem that could be greatly increased by the warmer water. Yet, incredibly, not one of the plants is installing cooling towers to reduce the environmental impact of the heated water on this vital segment of the Great Lakes chain—a major resource of international importance.

On a nationwide basis, more than 100 nuclear power plants will be installed within the next five years. By 1980, the electric power industry—with both nuclear and fossil fuel plants—will be using one-fifth of the total fresh water runoff in the United States for cooling.

The tragedy of what is happening to the Great Lakes is clearly one of the ugliest examples of stupidity and greed. The pollution sequence has reached the point where Lake Erie is nearly destroyed, with Lake Michigan close behind, and Lakes Huron and Ontario gravely threatened. Only Lake Superior, the third largest body of fresh water on earth—almost 3000 cubic miles—is still clean.

Just how long Lake Superior will remain clean is highly questionable. The threat to its sparkling blue waters has begun. The Reserve Mining Company, owned by the Republic Steel and Armco Steel corporations, is dumping into these waters more than 60,000 tons of wastes daily from its taconite—low grade iron ore—processing plant. It has been computed that, if the plant operates at current levels for the next forty years, it will dump into the lake one trillion, 881 billion, 600 million pounds of taconite tailings.

Federal reports have concluded that the waste discharge is already damaging the fragile ecology in the lake, is affecting the mineral content and the clarity of the water, and is destroying the already limited fish spawning grounds. There is little question that the wastes are polluting the lake.

To do the things that have to be done, the costs will be great. It will take vast Federal expenditures just to begin an environmental clean-up program. At least $20 billion to $25 billion a year over present expenditures is essential. Even if you estimate the investment to be $275 billion by the year 2000, there is no reason to consider that a staggering sum when you remember it is equivalent to this country's defense expenditures for the next four years, not to mention the billions spent on space adventure. Until this nation makes the same kind of commitment to environmental preservation that it made in building the most massive defense machine in history or in sending men to the moon, the battle cannot be won.

We must not feel, however, that spending of this magnitude will, by itself, solve our environmental crisis. But, it will buy us a beginning. Before the environmental crisis is even close to being resolved, everyone will be involved in paying part of the cost. Since the automobile internal combustion engine is the major contributor to air pollution—an estimated sixty per cent nationwide—a pollution-free engine will have to be developed. This will be an expensive research and retooling dilemma for the automobile industry, and in the end it is likely that future cars will be more expensive and have less power.

The nation's insatiable demand for electricity is another example. The power companies are arguing that they will not be able to keep up with the demands for increased power within the next ten years, unless they can build nuclear power plants. Each multi-million dollar nuclear power plant needs millions of gallons of water daily to cool the machinery. But when that water is ejected into a lake or river at increased temperatures, it upsets the ecology system, speeds up the growth of oxygen-stealing algae, and kills fish. Construction of the necessary cooling equipment to expel the used water at the proper temperatures will make each plant much more expensive and will probably increase electric bills for users. In the long run, many Americans may have to get used to living without many of the electronic frills to which we all have become so accustomed.

In addition to Federal monies, great sums will have to be spent by state and local governments and by the private sector. It is difficult at this time to give even a rough estimate of the amount at stake here because I don't think anyone has made a study. If we do what we want to do—establish air and water quality standards for industry, for example, that become progressively more stringent as we develop more sophisticated waste and air pollution treatment equipment and insist that everyone comply—I don't think anyone has attempted to estimate what it would really cost to do this. It would, of course, be a cost that would continue to increase indefinitely until we have developed perfect equipment. But that cost must be measured against the cost we will pay if we don't do something. The best estimate we can get of the economic damage done by air pollution now is $10 billion to $12 billion a year. Well, obviously it isn't going to cost $10 billion to $12 billion indefinitely to stop air pollution.

Much controversy has arisen over who will bear the brunt of these costs. The governmental expenditures—whether Federal, state, or local—will, of course, ultimately be borne by the taxpayers. And the costs to the private sector will also probably be passed on to the consumer. I assume that some costs will be absorbed by industry, which has been a major contributor to environmental pollution, but the fact of the matter is that whatever adds to the cost of production adds to the cost of the product. If you are looking at it as a consumer, you have to decide how much you are going to pay if you don't accept some higher product costs. You are going to pay a tremendous amount of money, and it is going to be much more if you allow the environment to deteriorate than if you stop it.

Take water, for example. In the big metropolitan areas, we will have to use the same water ten, fifteen, or twenty times because we will be using the total national supply by the year 1980 and twice the total national supply by the year 2000. So let's assume that we don't do anything about stopping water pollution. The cost will be there in any event, because we will have to clean up all the water before we use it, and if you return it to the source dirty, then the next user will have to pull it out dirty and launder it. The point is, it doesn't matter what it costs to stop pollution, it will cost us several times as much not to stop. There is no way to avoid the cost. It is cheaper to pay the cost to stop pollution than to allow pollution to continue.

It will take much more than money to restore the environment. Cleaning up our environment and establishing quality on a par with quantity as a goal of American life will require a reshaping of our values, sweeping changes in the performance and goals of our institutions, national standards of quality for the goods we produce, a humanizing and redirection of our technology, and greatly increased attention to the problem of our expanding population.

Perhaps, most of all, it will require on the part of the people a new assertion of environmental rights and the evolution of an ecological ethic of understanding and respect for the bonds that unite the species man with the natural systems of the planet.

The ecological ethic must be debated and evolved by individuals and institutions on the terms of man's interdependence with nature. American acceptance of the ecological ethic will involve nothing less than achieving a transition from the consumer society to a society of "new citizenship"—a society that concerns itself as much with the well-being of present and future generations as it does with bigness and abundance. It is an ethic whose yardstick for progress should be: Is it good for people? There is a great need and growing support for the introduction of new values in our society—where bigger is not necessarily better—where slower can be faster —where less can be more.

Perhaps man, with his rampaging breeding and indifference, has reached the point where much of the world he lives in will be nothing more than an area of poisonous waters and choking air surrounded by mountains of garbage and debris. With many municipalities already faced with a monumental problem of garbage disposal, it is estimated that every man, woman, and child in this country is now generating five pounds of refuse a day from household, commercial, and industrial uses. This refuse adds up to more than *365 billion pounds* a year.

Instead of using the country's impressive technology which made it possible to land man on the moon and develop super-mechanical devices capable of solving astronomical problems, the typically American approach is to take the easy way—dump the debris and garbage in the ocean.

Why shouldn't the municipal governments and business and industry believe the ocean would be a good dumping place? The sea bottom is already being used for dumping radioactive wastes, and until the Army was stopped recently, some thoughtful military bureaucrat decided it would be a great place to dump discarded poison gases. Perhaps previous dumping has caused some of the mysterious events and massive sea kills I have described.

The oceans are not a limitless funnel that take the chemical wastes and other debris to a magical "somewhere else" where they can be forgotten. More than twenty years ago, Los Angeles found that its beaches were contaminated and had to be closed to bathers because the city was not sterilizing its sewage. It was also discovered that wastes pumped by England into the North Sea were damaging Grand Banks fisheries off Newfoundland. The Japanese, concerned about their valuable fishing industry, have wisely banned dumping sewage into the sea.

It is the economic profit to be found in the sea that attracts and brings closer the threat of cataclysm which Dr. Paul Ehrlich, the noted ecologist, projected recently. He predicted that unless current trends are reversed, the oceans could end as a significant source of life in ten years with the end of man coming a short time later.

The massive oil leaks off Santa Barbara, California, which killed fish and sea fowl, and the huge oil leak from Los Angeles to the Gulf of Mexico could be the first dramatic warnings of this end. Other commercial ventures are under consideration as developers look to the possibilities of rich returns from moving parts of crammed megalopolis to floating cities. One developer is considering a floating jetport in the ocean waters off New York City, and airports off other cities are under study. Such facilities might well be beyond the reach of enforcement of any Federal agency regulations.

Unfortunately, there is a great deal of confusion and litigation concerning whether various ocean waters are public, private, national, or international. It seems to be a wild utopian dream that the world will be able to face the threat to the oceans in any reasonable way in the face of the fact that various government jurisdictions in this country cannot get together to develop responsible control programs for a simpler problem— domestic pollution.

Without agreements or strong regulations, the massive business and industrial corporations are at it again—this time it is frontier days on the high seas, and it's full speed ahead, damn the last clean environment on earth.

To date, 8000 oil wells have been drilled on the outer continental shelf. And little mention is made of the fact that the outer shelf is really 823 thousand square miles of undersea public domain, *owned by the people of the United States*. This public domain was once much greater. But in 1953, with the Submerged Lands Act, Congress gave outright, to the states, the first three miles of offshore seabed.

Our undersea domain is not the only ocean area that is threatened. Landward, our coastline environment is becoming an unmanageable tangle of conflicting, polluting uses that eliminate wetlands, destroy shellfish and other valuable sea life in sensitive estuaries, wipe out beaches with unwise development, and degrade the natural values that make our coastline areas perhaps the most vital recreation resource in the nation.

The Federal government should halt all aid for development that would affect the coastal environment until plans meeting national criteria are developed. And on the outer continental shelf—the vast undersea region extending beyond the coast—the Secretary of the Interior should grant no more leases of any kind until similar environmental criteria can be developed to protect this vital last frontier. In fact, untapped ocean deposits of oil and other minerals under the Secretary's jurisdiction should be held in a National Marine Mineral Resources trust until we know enough to avoid the environmental disasters that could result from their extraction, and I have introduced legislation which would require this.

The real loser in man's greedy drive is the youth of this country and the world. Because of the stupidity of their elders, the children of today face an ugly world in the near future, with dangerously and deadly polluted air and water; overcrowded development; festering mounds of debris; and an insufficient amount of open space to get away from it all.

Since youth is again the great loser, perhaps the only hope for saving the environment and putting quality back into life may well depend on our being able to tap the energy, idealism, and drive of the oncoming generation that, otherwise, will inherit the poisonous air and deadly waters of the earth.

Biologist Barry Commoner, chairman of the St. Louis Committee for Environmental Information, warned recently that "we don't really know what the long-term effects of various types of environmental deterioration will be, and the kids are the guinea pigs."

Fortunately, the rising generation appears not to be content to be the guinea pigs of a society that has lost its sense of priority. One of the most dramatic developments of this decade has been the insistence of youth that in the last third of the Twentieth Century, the quality of life must have a much higher priority than the greed of past generations has permitted. A few random examples:

¶ On learning that the United Nations is planning to hold a world conference on the environment in 1972, the youth of several nations have called for an International Youth Assembly on the environment in 1971 to give notice to the world's leaders that their generation realizes it is they who suffer most from a destroyed environment.

¶ A group of high school juniors in Ashland, Wisconsin, recently showed concern for the growing threat to the ecology of Lake Superior by demonstrating in support of Duluth's Pollution Enforcement Conference. They were demanding a clean lake.

¶ The same concern was voiced by a Washington, D.C., university student who, when told that a Congressional proposal to bring a complete halt to any Federal program that damaged the environment might be unconstitutional, asked: "Isn't polluting our rivers unconstitutional?"

It is also clear that preservation and protection of the environment must be one of the highest national priorities. To that end, I have proposed a Constitutional amendment that states: "Every person has the inalienable right to a decent environment. The United States and every state shall guarantee this right." This legislation has been introduced because the environmental crisis is the greatest single threat to our pursuit of the inalienable rights of life, liberty, and the pursuit of happiness. The tragedy is that the citizen has few clear legal or constitutional avenues to protect the sensitivities and the well-being of himself, his family, or his community from environmental assault.

Far too frequently, the citizen finds himself left with no remedy in the fact of the pollution of a lake which belongs to the public or the poisoning of the air which he must breathe or the shattering din which is imposed upon him. Our Anglo-Saxon common law tradition has focused protection on economic or personal injury. We are learning now, however, that environmental damages can be just as severe. If this amendment passes the Congress and is ratified by the states, it will lay the groundwork for further definition in the statutes at the Federal and state levels and by the courts, making environmental reform the right and goal of all Americans.

Further, we must establish national policies on land use, on air and water quality, on resource management, on the ocean's development and use, and on population. We must institute a new effort to keep pesticides, herbicides, detergents, and fuel additives and the vast cross section of products out of the marketplace until they are tested and meet environmental and health standards.

Each year new species of animals are added to the list of those soon to be extinct. Man in his arrogance appears to think that he can escape joining that list. The evidence is overwhelming, however, that it is much later than he realizes, that the species Man cannot long watch the animals disappear without seeing that his end, too, is coming. Man, ironically, may be the creature that left as his monument a planet nearly as incapable of sustaining life as its barren neighbors in the dead vacuum of the solar system we are now exploring at costs that are fantastically greater than we are prepared to spend to preserve our own planet.

The Environmental Crisis in the Context of American Politics

by HAROLD SPROUT

HAROLD SPROUT, *one of America's most distinguished political scientists, is a research associate with the Center of International Studies at Princeton University. He is also Professor Emeritus, Department of Politics, at the school. A widely read author, he has written numerous books, papers, and monographs in his field.*

From: An abridgement of a paper presented by Harold Sprout to the Princeton University Conference on Ecology and Politics in America's Environmetal Crisis, March 6, 1970. Copyright © 1970 by Princeton University. Reprinted with permission from University: A Princeton Quarterly.

Environmental deterioration in America has reached a stage of crisis, in part "because major changes in priorities accompanied by massive changes in the allocation of resources are needed to arrest and reverse the current ruinous trend. . . ."

My discussion is built around two theses in particular. First, there is need for a stronger and more widespread sense of urgency in order to sustain environmental programs that, in order to be effective, will inevitably be severely restrictive and very expensive. Second, environmental imperatives are competing with a multiplicity of rising demands for scarce resources, with the outcome far from certain.

Before proceeding with these propositions, a few words on some preliminary matters: . . . Use of the word "environment": I shall use *environment* and *environmental* with reference to nonhuman physical surroundings. When referring to urban squalor, poverty, inequality, and the like, I shall use the adjective *social* even though such things are part of environment broadly defined.

The viewpoint from which I speak: I am, and I have long been, committed to environmental protection and improvement. But my role here is not to argue this cause. . . . My task is rather to point out some of the conditions that seem likely to influence both what is attempted and how well that attempt can be carried out.

Now, to the main issues: I take off from the truism that what matters in the making of policies is not how conditions actually are, but how these are perceived by those who participate in the process. Applied to the environmental crisis, this distinction is between conditions as *professional ecologists and other relevant experts declare these to be,* and as *non-expert lawmakers and citizens believe them to be.*

This distinction becomes especially important when the ultimate effects of a current situation are not immediately obvious. Such is notably the case with environmental pollution. For example, adverse effects of poisoned air on health may not become fully evident for ten to twenty years or more.

Plainly, 99-plus percent of the American people (including most elected lawmakers) have little or no expert knowledge of ecological cycles, ecosystems, or the ramifying consequences of environmental changes. They are about as ill-equipped to assess the longer-range effects of foul air, as they would be to describe the mechanisms of a space rocket. But however limited their ecological knowledge, citizens have votes. And their elected representatives determine priorities, levy taxes, and allocate scarce resources.

There is a well-known tendency to dismiss expert predictions as unproved conjectures. This tendency is especially strong if the policy implications threaten vested interests and cherished freedoms and amenities. Thus, the first question to ask about the political context of our environmental crisis is: *How is this crisis perceived by politicians and citizens generally?* Is there a widespread sense of peril? If so, is it sufficient to sustain restrictive and very costly courses of action?

. . . Most Americans are at least intermittently and unpleasantly aware of smog, polluted water, excessive noise, rising mountains of debris, and other evidence of our deteriorating environment. Opinion polls indicate that a majority favor doing something about it. One notes, in particular, that environmental quality is becoming a serious concern of students all over the country. Some observers assert that public opinion is "forcing the pace" for environmental improvement.

However, we have little basis as yet for predicting how much Americans are willing to pay for a cleaner and more salubrious environment. How will they react when they begin to feel the pinch in their accustomed style of life? How will they respond to higher taxes and higher prices that will certainly accompany significant environmental programs? My impression is that most people are reluctant even to talk about such an unpalatable prospect.

Put this another way: It is doubtful if any but the tiniest minority—chiefly scientists and dedicated conservationists—believe as yet that conditions are sufficiently menacing to justify drastic remedies. It is still more doubtful if any substantial number of Americans believe the experts who insist that continuation of present trends could render the earth uninhabitable within two or three generations. Such a possibility is simply beyond the comprehension of most people.

In short, there is clearly a spreading awareness of environmental deterioration. There is apparently a widespread and growing desire to do something. But I can find little evidence that any large number of Americans are ready as yet to pay a high personal price to achieve environmental goals. And it is notorious that important agencies of government, strongly supported by influential bodies of citizens, cling tenaciously to ongoing programs and new projects—for example in agriculture, and in air transport, among others—that promise to make conditions worse rather than better. . . .

Moreover, this is only half of the picture. *Environmental imperatives are competing with other massive demands on scarce resources.* Available goods and services are never sufficient to cover demands in any society. But I can think of no time (except possibly the final months of World War II) when the gap between demands and disposable resources in America has been so wide as it has become today. For this reason, it is needful to examine environmental programs within the context of a larger American crisis—a crisis that has been aptly called the *crisis of priorities.*

This larger crisis has many roots. But three are chiefly responsible for its intractability as well as centrality in American politics today. One of these is the *size and inflexibility of the military budget.* The second is the *rising demand for action to arrest environmental deterioration.* The third is a concomitant *massive rise in demands for a cluster of social needs* associated with poverty, education, the cities, and other urgent social problems. . . .

In 1960 the military departments received 50 percent of all monies disbursed through the Federal government. By 1969, total dollar expenditures by those departments had risen from $38 billions, to $77 billions. Much of this increase was for the war in Vietnam. Some of it was inflation of prices largely attributable to the war. Thus, during the 1960's, the percentage of Federal expenditures allocated to the military establishment declined slightly. But at the end of the decade it still amounted to 45 percent of the Federal budget. Recent decisions promise some further reduction—but how much remains to be seen. . . .

It has been repeatedly asserted that Federal spending for military purposes could be reduced by as much as 50 percent without any real loss of security. This is, of course, debatable. But it is not debatable that the Federal government lacks adequate procedures for weighing rationally the demands of the military against those of the civil society. Hitherto, the absence of rational allocation procedures has worked mainly to the advantage of the military establishment. In the changing climate of American politics, it may work increasingly in the opposite direction. In any case, given a taxing system as rigid as ours, the huge military budget is an obvious and attractive alternative source of large funds needed for domestic civilian purposes.

There is some tendency on the part of ecologists and dedicated conservationists to assume that a cleaner and quieter environment is a universal value. This may well be so from a physiological perspective. But it is by no means so from a political perspective. Environmental values are strongly identified with the higher income classes—notably those in the top 20 percent who receive over 40 percent of all distributed income.

From the standpoint of the less affluent, environmental values rank somewhat lower. They tend to be regarded as luxuries until more elemental needs are satisfied. . . . When exhorted about the virtues of clean air, pure water, noise abatement, unlittered landscape, and the rest, the poor and near-poor are generally unimpressed. . . .

There was a time—not so long ago—when the millions who fall into this category constituted the "invisible poor." They were invisible in the sense that those who ruled knew little about their needs, and did next to nothing to alleviate their condition. The poor were ignorant and unorganized. They had little or no effective access to the government that ruled ostensibly on their behalf. They were, in effect, aliens in the society of which they were nominal members.

It is not news that times have changed. Those who speak for the poor and near-poor can make their demands heard, and oftener heeded than formerly—thanks in part to leadership and organization. But their rising political potential springs also from another source. That is their tightening grip on essential services in our easily disrupted urban society. What this might portend was fleetingly revealed in the sanitation workers' strike of 1967 in New York City. It was revealed again in the more recent firemen's strike in Gary. It was starkly evident in the chaos produced in a single day by the police strike in Montreal.

In short, demands on behalf of the less affluent members of our society are acquiring a muscle that makes these people increasingly formidable claimants in the competition for scarce resources. And most of their spokesmen, I repeat, do not put environmental values first. Specifically, I am suggesting that any program for spending large sums for cleaner air, water, and the rest will run into grave political trouble if these values are put ahead of comparable outlays to eradicate poverty and the consequences of poverty.

So far as I am aware, no one has yet offered a carefully researched estimate of the overall cost of repairing a century and more of environmental exploitation and neglect. Or how much it will cost to prevent further serious deterioration. Conservative guesses run to "tens of billions of dollars annually. . . ." Furthermore, estimates of cost are escalating as more is learned about the magnitude and technical complexities of the problems that confront us.

A salient feature of the present situation is the simultaneous peaking of demands for social and for environmental reform. These combined demands present a picture of needed future outlays for the domestic society that are more nearly comparable to the cost of World War II than of the war in Vietnam. . . . But there are still other, if lesser, claimants for scarce resources. These include the modernizing countries which have come to depend upon us for economic and technical assistance—and in whose political future we profess to have a vital interest. There are demands for further research and sorties into outer space, for supersonic air transports, and for other expensive projects on the scientific and engineering frontiers. There are escalating demands for more police and stronger law enforcement generally, and for many other things deemed essential by politically influential segments of our national community.

This peaking of demands and costs in nearly every sector of public expenditure bedevils policy making at all levels of government. Plainly, we are in for radical changes of priorities. But what changes?

Some, though perhaps a diminishing number, continue to give highest priority to military power on a scale sufficient to sustain all or most of the vast and scattered commitments built up around the world during the past generation. From any standpoint, military defense is a vital concern. Whether fighting wars in Asia or other distant places is essential to defense is hotly debated. One thing seems certain, however. *Barring drastic changes in the international climate, such questions will no longer be decided without regard for the impact of military commitments on our domestic society and habitat.* Specifically, the environmental and social crises present major challenges to previous modes of determining the size of military budgets. The strength of these challenges is a new factor in American politics. . . .

Obviously, there can be no quick or clean solution to this dispute over priorities. Massive changes in the allocation of resources could not be carried out overnight, or even in a year or two, within a political system so bureaucratized and rigid as ours has become. Equally obvious, the domestic crisis is not going to subside, simply by being ignored. Nor will palliative remedies cure our environmental malaise.

Reduced to elementals, there appear to be three ways to mobilize resources on the scale needed to check environmental deterioration and provide for future protection and maintenance. One way is to reduce still further the allocations to military-related purposes. A second is to provide more revenue by raising taxes. A third way is to push much of the cost onto private business with the expectation that most or all will be passed along to consumers in higher prices for automobiles, power, food, newspapers, and nearly everything else.

The present strategy in Washington seems to favor the third, reject the second, and resort to the first as little as possible. This strategy is accompanied by manifestly sincere efforts to liquidate the Vietnam war, reduce other commitments overseas, and reach a more comprehensive detente with the Russians. But it is also accompanied by severe curtailment of ongoing and promised social programs.

This strategy has obvious limitations. It can free only a small fraction of the resources required to check the worsening environmental crisis. Cutbacks of social programs and prospects of higher consumer prices are likely to intensify the opposition of those who give first priority to poverty, the cities, and social services in general. . . . Financing environmental programs through the market place is as inequitable to citizens of low income as are the regressive sales taxes upon which most of our states depend so heavily. For reasons previously discussed, stiffened opposition from the social sector could seriously blunt the thrust of any environmental program.

Other strategies may be lurking in the wings. . . . What might happen, for instance, if a legislative coalition should take form between those who are carrying torches for social and for environmental reform? Would not the obvious basis for such a coalition be to mobilize support for a more drastic assault on the military budget?

It would be easy to close on a note of pessimism. To do so would be to ignore much in the picture that is more encouraging. Not since the Japanese attack on Pearl Harbor has any public issue received such massive support in all the news media, local as well as national. Restoration of environmental quality has become a concern of students that may approach in scale and intensity their opposition to the war in Vietnam. More and more politicians are finding it a congenial issue. The President and numerous governors have spoken out strongly, as have leading members of Congress and state legislatures. Larger sums have already been allocated than one could reasonably have anticipated ten years ago. Civic organizations of many kinds are supporting the cause in scores if not hundreds of communities across the country. Increasingly, some of the most influential leaders of industry are identifying with the demand for a cleaner and more healthful environment.

A few, chiefly some of the more gross polluters, speak bitterly as if the environmental crisis were a synthetic fad manufactured by fanatics. But it is notable how relatively few such vocal dissenters there are, and how mildly they complain—at least in public.

One can cast up the account to date, and demur that all this is far from enough. And this is clearly so. But considering the rigidity and inertia of our political system, the diversity and magnitude of demands on disposable resources, and traditional American attitudes toward the earth and its subhuman inhabitants, one might conclude that what has been accomplished thus far represents a stronger beginning than might have been expected even three or four years ago.

Youth Speaks Up

Earth Day:
A Beginning

by DENIS HAYES

ARTICLES ON ecology generally tend to lead off with lists of disasters. But the shock effect of disasters is gone. Today such lists may even be counter-productive. They suggest we have a number of specific problems we must address. We don't. We have THE PROBLEM. All ecological concerns are interrelated parts of the problem of perpetuating life on this frail planet, and our approach to them must be holistic. It is abso-

DENIS HAYES, *a graduate of Stanford University, is entered at the Kennedy School of Government and the Law School at Harvard. He is now on leave to serve full-time as the national coordinator of Environmental Action.*

lute folly to continue to pursue piecemeal solutions—
when we know full well that the pesticides, the detergents, and the dams are all fouling the same river.

This is not to say that the new ecologists *oppose*
patchwork improvements—only that we're fairly indifferent to them. If bandages and baling wire make life
a little better, that's fine. But the cosmetic alterations
being offered by our politicians and our industrialists
don't really speak to THE PROBLEM at all. They are
the kinds of marginal compromises that a skillful play-
er makes to keep control of the game. The precedents
are clear.

Other social movements have tramped across the
dusty American stage. Many began in search of fundamental change; all failed. Our movement must be
different.

Until recently, American movements tended to have
a vulnerability. Relying heavily upon an economic analysis, they tended to focus at least in part upon material
goals. And this made them vulnerable. The American
economy can manufacture wondrous quantities of goods.
So if a militant group wanted a piece of the pie, and
was willing to fight for it, the economy would simply
produce a little more pie and give it some. And with
its material goals addressed, the movement invariably
lost its teeth.

The contemporary revolution, however, does not rely
upon an exclusively economic analysis, and its goals are
not acquisitive. It will be impossible to "buy off" the
peace people, to "buy off" the hippies, to "buy off"
the young Black militants, to "buy off" the ecology
freaks.

We can't be bought, because we demand something
the existing order can't produce. We demand a lower
productivity and a wider distribution. We demand
things which last, which can be used and reused. We
demand less arbitrary authority, and more decentral-
ization of power. We demand a fundamental respect
for nature, including man—even though this may some-

times result in "inefficiency."

Dissident groups accentuate different concerns, but our fundamental goals tend to be shared: ending exploitation, imperialism, and the war-based economy; guaranteeing justice, dignity, education, and health to all men. A focus on one concern does not mean a neglect of the others: We are able to seek more than one goal at a time. Those of us who have fought against the war will continue to do so until it is ended; those who have sought racial justice will not be satisfied until it is realized.

All these goals fall under a single unified value structure. This value is difficult to articulate, but posited most simply it might read: "the affirmation of life." This is a clear contradiction of most things for which America stands.

America is the New Rome, and is making Vietnam the new Carthage—razing her villages to the ground and salting what remains of her fields with long-lasting defoliants. America is the new Robber Baron—stealing from the poor countries of the world to satiate a gluttonous need for consumption. We waste our riches in planned obsolescence, and invest the overwhelming bulk of our national budget in ABMs and MIRVs and other means of death. Each of our biggest bombs today is the explosive equivalent of a cube of TNT as tall as the Empire State Building. And the only reason we don't have bigger bombs is that we don't have a means of delivering bigger bombs. Yet.

At the same time we are systematically destroying our land, our streams, and our seas. We foul our air, deaden our senses, and pollute our bodies. And it's getting worse. Our population and our rate of "progress" are both expanding geometrically. Tens of thousands could die in Los Angeles in a thermal inversion which is now probably unavoidable—and not one element of the existing system of air pollution control can do a thing to reduce the flow of poisonous traffic into that city. That's what America has become, and that's what we are challenging.

America has become indifferent to life, reducing that vibrant miracle to a dead statistic. This callousness has allowed us to overlook the modest, intermediate consequences of our crimes. If 50,000 people are killed, if ten million people starve, if an entire country is laid waste—we have learned to tuck the information into the proper file and write the affair off as a mistake.

We have to "unlearn" that. These aren't mistakes at all; they are the natural offshoots of the "growth generation"—of the neo-Keynesian mentality that *still* expects to find salvation in the continued growth of population and production. Nurtured in our frontier heritage as the short-sighted inhabitants of a bountiful, underpopulated country, this mental set (found in every economic text in our schools) has yet to grapple with the elementary fact that infinite expansion is impossible on a finite planet.

The implications of these old myths in the current setting are enormous. We now have the potential to destroy life on the planet, and in our rapacious plundering we are flirting with some frightening probabilities that we will do just that.

In a society in which death has lost its horror, with the slaughter of three wars under our belts and our streets full of mugging and indifference, a group of people—mostly young—is beginning to stand up and say, "No." We are beginning to say, simply, "We affirm life —a life in harmony with Nature." And that's what the youth crusade on environment is really all about.

Thousands of campuses and communities all across America have taken part in Earth Day. Each sought to focus its attention upon the degradation of its local environment. Each is trying to develop a holistic strategy for improvement. Some local groups are going to be reasonably moderate; others will be much more militant. None has any illusions about turning America around in one day, or one week, or one year. But it's a beginning.

It's a chance to start getting a handle on it all; a rejection of the silly idea that somehow bigger is better, and faster is better, world without limit, amen. This has never been true. It presumes infinite resources, and it presumes a mastery by Man over Nature, and over Nature's laws. Instead of seeking harmony, man has sought to subdue the whole world. The consequences of that are beginning to come home. And time is running out.

Sometimes, around dawn, we finish the previous day's work and I go for a walk. The sky slowly lightens, and in time the streets become snarled. People jostle around me, rushing from their dissatisfied homes to their unhappy places of labor. And they seem to know something is wrong. The Blacks, and the Wallace working class, the great silent majority—all feel the tense unease.

What's wrong is that the species is breaking the most fundamental biological rule; much of it seems unwilling to fight for its life. At a time when survival itself depends upon the development of an ecologically balanced world, the worshippers of "progress" are instead embracing death.

The inconsistencies are becoming clearer, and a whole generation is rapidly losing its naivete. A pregnant new politics is developing, which cuts across former boundaries and which scorns the sterile inflexibility of existing institutions.

We are mapping a struggle—not only against the vested interests of the giant corporations, not only against the paid-off senility in our Congress, not only against the Strangeloves in the Pentagon. Survival demands something more. The very survival of the species has come to demand an ecologically-balanced planet —a state at variance with most of the value assumptions of Western civilization. Our challenge must consider not only the pieces but the whole.

The course ahead is dangerous and complex and may be impossible. But new bonds of brotherhood are rapidly linking diverse people around a profoundly simple value: the affirmation of life. And with intelligence, courage, and luck, we may win.

A Not
So Silent Spring

by GLADWIN HILL

T HE WEEKEND of the Vietnam protest march last
November, 200 students from forty California colleges met at Stanford University for quite a different
purpose. It was to form a federation of campus organizations concerned with environmental problems, from
pollution to birth control.

The chairman of the meeting, a Stanford student
named Glenn Lopez, half apologized for the digression
from the cause at that moment preoccupying millions
of other students across the country. The environmental
weekend, he explained, had been scheduled and organized long before the Vietnam demonstration and could
not be changed. Moreover, he added trenchantly:
"Both activities are working toward the same goal: the
survival of the human race."

GLADWIN HILL *is the national environmental
correspondent of* The New York Times.

---

*Reprinted by permission of the William Morris Agency,
Inc. on behalf of Gladwin Hill.*

There was no need for apologies. The Stanford meeting was a milestone in what may become the greatest movement ever to sweep the country: the environmental revolution.

The environmental revolution is a sudden, remarkable, spontaneous rebellion not of one group against another so much as of everybody against the physical conditions to which two centuries of promiscuous "progress" have brought us—a world where ugliness is endemic, where corporeal hazards are rife, and where the issue of actual human survival suddenly has become poignantly explicit. And it is young people who are the vanguard of that revolution.

Humans, like all animals, display a remarkable, if often lamentable, capacity for adjusting themselves to their surroundings. That is what the adult world has done. But we now have a whole generation of young people under thirty, 100 million strong, who have the insight and perception to look around and appraise conditions objectively. And they have pronounced them appalling. They have said: "Look—the emperor has no clothes on."

The instantaneous, inexorable urge for reform has been more than mere criticism. Everybody knows by now that for countless young people anywhere in the country this is the prime topic of concern. A week after the Stanford conference, it was young people who ran away with a stodgy environmental-problems conference of the U.S. Commission for UNESCO in San Francisco. Tired of the verbiage with which generations of adults have avoided a meaningful confrontation with conditions, they maneuvered the meeting into endorsing, "unofficially," demands on President Nixon to take forthright action on prime problems of the day. A week later a youth bloc repeated the performance at a leaden conference in Los Angeles convoked by Governor Ronald Reagan as a pro forma bow to conservation but which ended up with a stirring summons to action, which subsequently has begun to materialize.

The youth crusade raises many questions. How substantial and enduring does it promise to be? Where does it stand in relation to that other high concern of young people, Vietnam, and our other murky overseas involvements? Is this another "generation backlash" or can young people find common cause with their sluggish elders in radically reshaping a polluted world?

The answers to these questions are emerging daily, and they are uniformly good. One only has to attend any sort of conservation or environmental meeting anywhere in the country to be reassured by young people's interest, perspicacity, and zeal. Blue jeans or gray flannels, they comport themselves maturely. Their sense of organization and effectiveness far surpasses that of the average fumbling, windy, all-adult gathering.

What are they doing? To begin with, they are organizing. There is scarcely a college campus today that does not have one or more "ecology action" groups. The University of Hawaii has a score, each organized around a particular cause. But organization is not made, as it is so often in the adult world, the end-all. Parliamentary and bureaucratic mechanisms, such as the ubiquitous Committee, are rejected instinctively in favor of action. There's a creek on the edge of town that's full of junk? Let's go out and clean it up *now*. The college trustees are contemplating a dubious land deal? Let's mimeograph some fliers and start picketing the administration building, *now*.

Systematic effort is more common than the impulsive. At Boston University, students are collaborating with state officials on water pollution problems. At the University of Texas, students are getting out an environmental newsletter to acquaint people with issues. At Santa Barbara, they are challenging the state's right to run a highway through an ecologically choice marshland. At Northwestern, they are agitating against Abbott Laboratories' chemical discharges into Lake Michigan.

Stephanie Mills, slender and black-haired, is a prominent example of youthful activism. She is the girl who, at the Mills College commencement in Oakland, California, last June, declaimed as valedictorian that the world was such a mess she didn't propose to bring any babies into it. Now, still only twenty-one, she is a paid campaigner for Planned Parenthood in Oakland. But she also has become a sort of Joan of Arc of environmental reform, an ambassador between youth and the adult world, turning down lucrative lecture dates to appear at conservation meetings all over the country to articulate the problems we face and youth's demands for action.

Students are precipitating deep changes in college curricula. The closed-shop compartmentalization of the traditional "disciplines"—such as biology, chemistry, physics, botany, and geology—is being altered in favor of an eclectic approach. "You can't look at turbidity in a stream intelligently," Washington University's Professor Barry Commoner explains, "without having some knowledge about the banks of the stream and the forest that's growing twenty-five yards away." A new ecological course at the University of Oregon entitled "Can Man Survive?" was expected to draw 500 enrollees. More than 2,000 registered, and the initial class on January 13 brought the biggest academic turnout in the university's history—6,000 students.

In the area of research, students are the secret arsenal of the environmental revolution. Cleaning up the country and the world is going to take a vast amount of legislation, litigation, and administration. The underpinning of all these activities is information, data, facts—which youth distinctively has the energy and imagination to corral.

Finally, there is the realm of political action, in which the adult world has been delinquent and passive. A declaration by the youth bloc at the UNESCO meeting in San Francisco sketched the scope of this: ". . . . sending lobbyists to local, state, and national capitals . . . . drawing up proposals to be offered to competing candidates . . . . supporting officials who have taken a strong stand for a healthy environment . . . . campaigning against candidates whose positions don't make ecological sense . . . . and if no candidate makes any ecological sense, running and supporting our own candidates."

The February, 1970 issue of *Fortune* was devoted entirely to environment. Its issue of a year before, devoted entirely to the concerns of youth, had not mentioned environment. The Santa Barbara oil well blowout of January 28, 1969 was the Hiroshima bomb of the environmental revolution for both old and young. Clinching this new preoccupation for young people was the tapering off of the Vietnam war as an object of practical *"now"* action. "After you'd demonstrated and torn up your draft card, if you had one, what was there really you could do?" one student remarked. Environment, dramatized by Santa Barbara, was a burning issue, here, omnipresent—with a 200-year backlog of pollution to clean up.

Lawrence Lipton, perhaps the original hippie, summarized recently in his column in the underground *Los Angeles Free Press:* "A poisoned earth isn't worth fight-

The First Step

We're action-oriented politically. The first step is to create an awareness, so that each citizen won't feel the problems are hopeless. And I have hope. Someone like Ralph Nader, after all, has shown what can be done.

MIKE FINK
Ecology Action Center
University of Wisconsin
March, 1970

ing for, win, lose, or draw. The number one theater of war is now the war for ecological survival." New Lefters regard Vietnam and environmental enormities as opposite sides of the same coin of Establishmentism. Youthful vexation with physical conditions ties in closely with contempt for the mores of big business, which is responsible for so much pollution.

Youth's new concern conceivably could slacken with the inevitably slow pace of reform. But astute observers doubt it. Brock Evans, the Sierra Club's Northwestern proconsul and himself definitely in the youth bracket, says: "There's so much to be done, so much that anyone, whatever campus he's on or whatever community he's in, can latch onto with real satisfaction, that I look to see this interest growing rather than diminishing, regardless of what happens with Vietnam."

Environmental discontent inherently involves rejection of much of the status quo—rejection of prevailing physical conditions, rejection of the economic mores and governmental mechanisms that allowed these conditions to come about, rejection of the shibboleth of bigness, rejection even of the hallowed "right" of endlessly reproducing the human species.

The status-quo world is not going to be able to take these assaults with equanimity. The Department of Justice, to name one status-quo monolith, doesn't like the idea of citizen groups coming into court with environmental dissatisfactions and challenging, for instance, the decisions of Federal administrative agencies.

In several pending cases the Department is trying to prop up the hoary business-oriented concept that a complainant has to show substantial economic damage (not just destruction of a beautiful mountain-top view) to have "standing" in court. Otherwise, Federal lawyers said in a recent case, every Tom, Dick, and Harry will be running to the courts with complaints. Some people think that might be a good idea. It undoubtedly will be up to today's young guard—the countless environmentally minded law students across the country—to push this modernization of the law to a successful consummation.

Generally, however, there seems to be less of a generation gap on the environmental front than anywhere else. The intrinsic power of the youth-sparked environmental revolution is its catholicism. Whatever your ideology, personality, or intellectual bent, the water is just as dirty, the air just as smoggy, the dangers of DDT-laden fish just as alarming.

On the campus the environmental cause is drawing out supporters who wouldn't have dreamed of attending a football rally. A conspicuous feature of every environmental gathering is the mixture of gray heads and young people. The atmosphere is one of community of interest.

The old "conservation establishment"—organizations like the Sierra Club, the Izaak Walton League, the Audubon Society—was so small that it plainly is not something to worry about repudiating. Rather, the feeling now is like the evangelical "one big union" concept that once sparked the labor movement.

Collaboration between the youth bloc and the adult world on environmental issues is the rule rather than the exception. On many college campuses, progressive faculty members have been the prime movers in galvanizing the new interest. In some instances, teachers are quietly instigating undercover student investigations into local conditions as part of course work.

On youth's part there is a remarkable deference to the experience of age in tackling this new cosmos of challenges. At the Stanford conference, experts were invited from all over the country to sit in as counsellors of a dozen topic panels. One was California's resources director, Norman B. Livermore, Jr., half-suspect because of his career ties with exploitative industry. However, empathy between him and the students developed quickly. A fortnight later, when a hundred students invited belatedly to the Reagan environmental conference found themselves strapped for money for food, it was

Livermore who quietly wrote out a personal check to cover their needs.

California Governor Reagan is organizing a student advisory panel on environment. So is Secretary of the Interior Walter J. Hickel. Some are skeptical of such gestures. The gestures had better be genuine. Political sham is one of the things youth is quick to spot and as quick to expose.

The old-line conservation organizations are reaching out for youth. The Sierra Club, although never a gray-beard organization (since the day of its initial member, bearded John Muir), has established a new department for youth coordination—even though it was, in fact, Sierra Club chapters on a number of campuses that provided nuclei for the new movement.

Across the nation, the college environmental zealots seem more inclined to maintain the autonomous spontaneity of their own movements than to immerse themselves in the formalities of national organizations. But they will collaborate with "bird watchers," local civic groups, or with anybody who's going their way.

It's an encouraging and inspiring picture. At Santa Barbara's January observance of the first anniversary of the oil well blowout, a feature of the day was the promulgation of an "Environmental Bill of Rights" composed by a University of California professor, Roderick Nash. But he was upstaged, in the attention of observers, by his own eight-year-old daughter, a pig-tailed, outgoing little girl whose own painstakingly scrawled declaration in some ways outshone her father's lofty verbiage.

"The world I want," she wrote, "is like a lot of the world I saw last summer. We drank cold water from clear streams. We rode through big rapids . . . . I like fields where trees and flowers grow and forests where birds sing and chipmunks chatter.

"I would like to live in a world full of people who love it as much as I do. I hope my children's world is like that too."

To Prevent a World Wasteland

by GEORGE F. KENNAN

NOT even the most casual reader of the public prints of recent months and years could be unaware of the growing chorus of warnings from qualified scientists as to what industrial man is now doing—by overpopulation, by plundering of the earth's resources, and by a precipitate mechanization of many of life's processes —to the intactness of the natural environment on which his survival depends. "For the first time in the history

GEORGE F. KENNAN, *distinguished American diplomat and author, capped a long Foreign Service career by serving as U.S. Ambassador to the U.S.S.R. (1952-1953) and later to Yugoslavia (1961-1963). The author of numerous books and papers, he won the Pulitzer Prize in 1957 for* Russia Leaves the War. *He is currently a professor at the Institute for Advanced Study, Princeton, N.J., and President of the National Institute of Arts and Letters.*

From: Foreign Affairs, *Vol. 48, No. 3, April 1970. (New York: Council on Foreign Relations, Inc., © 1970). Used with permission.*

of mankind," U.N. Secretary-General U Thant wrote, "there is arising a crisis of worldwide proportions involving developed and developing countries alike—the crisis of human environment. . . . It is becoming apparent that if current trends continue, the future of life on earth could be endangered."

Study and debate of these problems, and sometimes even governmental action, have been developing with cumulative intensity. This response has naturally concentrated largely on environmental deterioration as a national problem. It is normally within national boundaries that the first painful effects of deterioration are felt. It is at the national level that the main burden of legislation and administrative effort will admittedly have to be borne, if certain kinds of pollution and destruction are to be halted.

But it is also clear that the national perspective is not the only one from which this problem needs to be approached. Polluted air does not hang forever over the country in which the pollution occurs. The contamination of coastal waters does not long remain solely the problem of the nation in whose waters it has its origin. Wildlife—fish, fowl, and animal—is no respecter of national boundaries, either in its movements or in the sources from which it draws its being. Indeed, the entire ecology of the planet is not arranged in national compartments; and whoever interferes seriously with it anywhere is doing something that is almost invariably of serious concern to the international community at large.

There is today in existence a considerable body of international arrangements, including several of great value, dealing with or affecting in one way or another the environmental problem. A formidable number of international organizations, some intergovernmental, some privately organized, some connected with the United Nations, some independently based, conduct programs in this field. As a rule, these programs are of a research nature. In most instances the relevance to problems of environmental conservation is incidental rather than central. While most of them are universal in focus, there are a few that approach the problem— and in some instances very usefully—at the regional level. Underlying a portion of these activities, and providing in some instances the legal basis for it, are a number of multilateral agreements that have environmental objectives or implications.

All this is useful and encouraging. But whether these activities are all that is needed is another question. Only a body fortified by extensive scientific expertise could accurately measure their adequacy to the needs at hand; and there is today, so far as the writer of these lines is aware, no body really charged with this purpose. In any case, it is evident that present activities have not halted or reversed environmental deterioration. . . .

. . . There is nothing today to give us the assurance that efforts will be made promptly enough, or on a sufficient scale, to prevent a further general deterioration in man's environment, a deterioration of such seriousness as to be in many respects irreparable. Even to the nonscientific layman, the conclusion seems inescapable that if this objective is to be achieved, there will have to be an international effort much more urgent in its timing, bolder and more comprehensive in its conception, and more vigorous in its execution than anything created or planned to date.

The General Assembly of the United Nations has not been indifferent to the gravity of this problem. Responding to the timely initiative and offer of hospitality of the Swedish government, it has authorized the Secretary-General to proceed at once with the preparation of a "United Nations Conference on the Human Environment," to be held at Stockholm in 1972. There is no question but that this undertaking, the initiation and pursuit of which does much credit to its authors, will be of major significance. But the conference will not be of an organizational nature; nor would it be suited to such a purpose. The critical study of existing vehicles for treating environmental questions internationally, as well as the creation of new organizational devices in this field, is a task that will have to be performed elsewhere. There is no reason why it should not be vigorously pursued even in advance of the Conference—indeed, it is desirable for a number of reasons that it should. As was stated in the Secretary-General's report, "the decision to convene the Conference, and the preparations for it, should in no way be used to postpone or to cancel already initiated or planned programs of research or cooperation, be they at the national, regional, or international level. On the contrary, the problems involved are so numerous and so complicated that all efforts to deal with them immediately should be continued and intensified." It will be useful to attempt to picture the functions that need to be performed if this purpose is to be achieved.

The first of these would be to provide adequate facilities for the collection, storage, retrieval, and dissemination of information on all aspects of the problem. This would involve not just assembling the results of scientific investigation but also keeping something in the nature of a register of all conservational activities at international, national, regional, and even local levels across the globe. The task here is not one of conducting original research but rather of collecting and collating the results of research done elsewhere, and disposing of that information in a manner to make it readily available to people everywhere.

A second function would be to promote the coordination of research and operational activities which now deal with environmental problems at the international level. The number of these is already formidable. To take a parallel from the American experience, it was calculated, when the President's Cabinet Committee on Environmental Quality was recently established in the White House, that there were al-

ready over 80 programs related to enivronmental questions being pursued just within the executive branch
of the Federal Government. If a similar census were
to be taken in the international field, the number
would scarcely be less. A recent listing of just those
bodies concerned with the peaceful uses of outer space
noted 17 entities.

These activities have grown up, for the most part,
without central structure or concept. There is not today
even any assurance, or any means of assuring, that they
cover all the necessary fields. The disadvantages of such
a situation—possibilities for confusion, duplication, and
omission—are obvious.

A third function would be to establish international
standards in environmental matters and to extend advice and help to individual governments and to regional organizations in their efforts to meet these standards. It is not a question here of giving orders, exert-
ing authority, or telling governments what to do. The
function is in part an advisory one and in part, no
doubt, hortatory: a matter of establishing and explaining requirements, of pressing governments to accept and
enforce standards, of helping them to overcome domestic opposition. The uses of an international authority,
when it comes to supporting and stiffening the efforts
of governments to prevail against commercial, industrial, and military interests within their respective jurisdictions, have already been demonstrated in other instances, as, for example, in the European Iron and
Steel Community. They should not be underestimated
here.

The fourth function that cries out for performance
is from the standpoint of the possibilities in international (as opposed to national or regional) action,
the most important of all. In contrast to all the others,
it relates only to what might be called the great international media of human activity: the high seas, the
stratosphere, outer space, perhaps also the Arctic and
Antarctic—media which are subject to the sovereign

authority of no national government. It consists simply of the establishment and enforcement of suitable rules for all human activities conducted in these media. It is a question not just of conservational considerations in the narrow sense but also of providing protection against the unfair exploitation of these media, above all the plundering or fouling or damaging of them, by individual governments or their nationals for selfish parochial purposes. Someone, after all, must decide at some point what is tolerable and permissible here and what is not; and since this is an area in which no sovereign government can make these determinations, some international authority must ultimately do so.

No one should be under any illusions about the far-reaching nature, and the gravity, of the problems that will have to be faced if this fourth function is to be effectively performed. There will have to be a determined attack on the problem of the "flags of convenience" for merchant shipping, and possibly their replacement by a single international régime and set of insignia for vessels plying the high seas. One will have to tackle on a hitherto unprecedented scale the thorny task of regulating industrialized fishing in international waters. There may have to be international patrol vessels charged with powers of enforcement in each of these fields. Systems of registration and licensing will have to be set up for uses made of the seabed as well as outer space; and one will have to confront, undaunted, the formidable array of interests already vested in the planting of oil rigs across the ocean floor.

For all of these purposes, the first step must be, of course, the achievement of adequate international consensus and authorization in the form of a multilateral treaty or convention. But for this there will have to be some suitable center of initiation, not to mention the instrument of enforcement which at a later point will have to come into the picture.

What sort of authority holds out the greatest promise of assuring the effective performance of these functions?

It must first be noted that most of them are now being performed in some respects and to some degree by international organizations of one sort or another. . . . Dozens of organizations collect information. Several make recommendations to governments. Some even exercise a limited coordinating role in individual fields. They cover a significant portion of needs; and they obviously cannot be ignored when it comes to the examination of the best organizational response to the problem in question. On the contrary, any approach that failed to take advantage of the work they are already accomplishing, any approach in particular that attempted to duplicate their present activity or to centralize it completely, would assuredly fail. But even in their entirety, they do not cover the whole spectrum of the functions that need to be performed, as listed above; and those that they do perform they perform, for the most part, inadequately.

The question therefore poses itself: How should these organizations be reinforced or expanded? Do they provide in themselves an adequate basis for the necessary expansion of function and activity? Or do they need to be supplemented by new organizational forms, and, if so, of what nature? Is there need for a central organization to bring all these activities under a single hat? Should there be several centers? Or none at all?

There is a view—and it is based on impressive experience and authority—which holds that there is no need for any unifying effort in these various forms of activity, at least not beyond such limited coördinating influence as United Nations bodies are able to exercise today; that any effort in this direction might only further confuse an already confused pattern; and that the most promising line of attack is for governments to intensify their support of activities already in progress, letting them develop separately according to function, letting one set of organizations continue to occupy itself with radiology, another with other forms of air pollution, another with the ecology of fresh water lakes and rivers, another with wildlife, another with oil pollution on the high seas, another with the ocean bed, etc. This is, of course, in many ways the easiest course. Existing efforts, under this procedure, are not disturbed. Existing arrangements for international control and support are not placed in question. Established competencies, sometimes conquered and defended in past years with much effort, are not jeopardized.

But there are weighty considerations that argue against such a course. . . . There is a considerable body of opinion, particularly in U.N. circles, to the effect that it is a mistake to separate the function of conservation and protection of natural resources from that of the development and exploitation of these resources for productive purposes. According to this view, there should not be separate organizations concerned with conservation. Considerations of an environmental nature should rather be built from the outset into all those activities that are concerned with the productive exploitation of natural resources, so that environmental needs would be met, so to speak, at the source.

This writer must respectfully disagree. This is an area in which exploitative motives cannot usefully be mingled with conservational ones. What is needed here is a watchdog; and the conscience and sense of duty of the watchdog must not be confused by contrary duties and undertakings. It may be boldly asserted that of the two purposes in question, conservation should come first. The principle should be that one exploits what a careful regard for the needs of conservation leaves to be exploited, not that one conserves with a liberal indulgence of the impulse to development leaves to be conserved.

What is lacking in the present pattern of approaches would seem to be precisely an organizational personality—part conscience, part voice—which has at heart the interests of no nation, no group of nations, no armed force, no political movement, and no commercial concern, but simply those of mankind generally, together—and this is important—with man's animal and vegetable companions, who have no other advocate. If determinations are to be made of what is desirable from the standpoint of environmental conservation and protection, then they are going to have to proceed from a source which, in addition to including scientific competence and having qualified access to all necessary scientific data, sees things from a perspective which no national body—and no international one whose function is to reconcile conflicting national interests—can provide.

The process of compromise of national interests will of course have to take place at some point in every struggle against environmental deterioration at the international level. But it should not occur in the initial determination of what is and is not desirable from the conservational standpoint. This determination should at first be made, so to speak, in its pure form, or as near as one can get to it. It should serve as the point of departure for the long, wearisome, often thorny and frustrating, road of accommodation that will have to be traversed before it can be transformed into reality. But it should not itself be compromised at the outset.

Nor is this the only reason why one cannot make do with just the reinforcement of what now exists. If the present process of deterioration is to be halted, things are going to have to be done which will encounter formidable resistance from individual governments and powerful interests within individual countries. Only an entity that has great prestige, great authority, and active support from centers of influence within the world's most powerful industrial and maritime nations will be able to make headway against such recalcitrance. One can conceive of a single organization's possessing such prestige and authority. It is harder to conceive of the purpose being served by some fifty to a hundred organizations, each active in a different field, all of them together presenting a pattern too complicated even to be understood or borne in mind by the world public.

All of this would seem to speak for the establishment of a single entity which, while not duplicating the work of existing organizations, could review this work from the standpoint of man's environmental needs as a whole, could make it its task to spot the inadequacies and identify the unfilled needs, could help to keep governments and leaders of opinion informed as to what ought to be done to meet minimum needs, could endeavor to assure that proper rules and standards are established wherever they are needed, and could, where desired, take a hand, vigorously and impartially, in the work of enforcement of rules and standards. It would not have to perform all these various functions itself— except perhaps where there was no one else to do so. Its responsibility should be rather to define their desirable dimensions and to exert itself, and use its influence with governments, to the end that all of them were performed by *someone,* and in an adequate way.

This entity, while naturally requiring the initiative of governments for its inception and their continued interest for its support, would have to be one in which the substantive decisions would be taken not on the basis of compromise among governmental representatives but on the basis of collaboration among scholars, scientists, experts, and perhaps also something in the nature of environmental statesmen and diplomats—but true international servants, bound by no national or political mandate, by nothing, in fact, other than dedication to the work at hand.

It is impossible to picture an entity of this nature without considering, in the first instance, the possible source of its initiation and sponsorship in the international community. Who would take the lead in establishing it? From whom would it draw its financial resources? Who would constitute the ultimate sanction for its existence and its authority?

Obviously no single government could stand as the patron for such an agency. To seek, on the other hand, the sanction of the entire international community for its inception and activity would scarcely be a promising undertaking. Aside from the fact that this would then necessitate procedures practically indistinguishable from those of the United Nations itself, it would mean involving in the control and operation of the entity to be established a host of smaller and less developed countries which could contribute very little to the solution of the problems at hand. It would also involve formidable delays and heavy problems of decision-taking. Were this to be the course selected, one would do better to content one's self, throughout, with the existing facilities of the United Nations, which represent just about the limit of what can be accomplished on the basis of a universal, or near-universal, governmental consensus.

One is driven to the conclusion that if anything very constructive is going to be accomplished along this line, the interest and initiative will have to proceed from a relatively small group of governments; and logic suggests that these should be those of the leading industrial and maritime nations. It is they whose economies produce, in the main, the problem of pollution. It is they, again, who have the means to correct it. It is they, finally, who have the scientific and other resources to analyze the problem and to identify the most promising lines of solution. The devastation of the environment is primarily, though not exclusively, a function of advanced industrial and urban society. The correction of it is primarily a problem for the advanced nations.

One can conceive, then, by an act of the imagination, of a small group of advanced nations, consisting of roughly the ten leading industrial nations of the world, including communist and noncommunist ones alike, together (mainly for reasons of their maritime interests) with the Scandinavians and perhaps with the

Benelux countries as a bloc, constituting themselves
something in the nature of a club for the preservation
of natural environment, and resolving, then, in that
capacity, to bring into being an entity—let us call it
initially an International Environmental Agency—
charged with the performance, at least on their behalf,
of the functions outlined above. It would not, however, be advisable that this agency should be staffed at
the operating level with governmental representatives
or that it should take its decisions on the basis of intergovernmental compromise. Its operating personnel
should rather have to consist primarily of people of
scientific or technical competence, and the less these
were bound by disciplinary relationships to individual
governments, the better. One can imagine, therefore,
that instead of staffing and controlling this agency
themselves, the governments in question might well in-
sert an intermediate layer of control by designating in
each case a major scientific institution from within
their jurisdiction—an Academy of Science or its equivalent—to act as a participating organization. These scientific bodies would then take over the responsibility
for staffing the agency and supervising its operations.
. . . The Soviet Academy of Sciences, if called upon
by its government to play a part in such an undertaking, would do so with an integrity and a seriousness of purpose worthy of its great scientific tradition,
and would prove a rock of strength for the accom-
plishment of the objectives in question.

The agency would require, of course, financial support from the sponsoring governments. There would
be no point in its establishment if one were not willing to support it generously and regularly; and one
should not underestimate the amount of money that
would be required. It might even run eventually to as
much as the one-hundredth part of the military budgets
of the respective governments for the same period of
time, which would of course be a very substantial sum.
Considering that the threat the agency would be de-

signed to confront would be one by no means less menacing or less urgent than those to which the military appropriations are ostensibly devoted, this could hardly be called exorbitant.

The first task of such an agency should be to establish the outstanding needs of environmental conservation in the several fields, to review critically the work and the prospects of organizations now in existence, in relation to those needs, to identify the main lacunae, and to make recommendations as to how they should be filled. Such recommendations might envisage the concentration of one or another sort of activity in a single organization. They might envisage the strengthening of certain organizations, the merging of others. They might suggest the substance of new multilateral treaty provisions necessary to supply the foundation for this or that function of regulation and control. They might involve the re-allotment of existing responsibility for the development of standards, or the creation of new responsibilities of this nature. In short, a primary function of the Agency would be to advise governments, regional organizations, and public opinion generally on what is needed to meet the environmental problem internationally, and to make recommendations as to how these needs can best be met. It would then of course be up to governments, the sponsoring ones and others as well, to implement these recommendations in whatever ways they might decide or agree on.

This, as will be seen, would be initially a process of study and advice. It would never be entirely completed; for situations would be constantly changing, new needs would be arising as old ones were met, the millennium would never be attained. But one could hope that eventually, as powers were accumulated and authority delegated under multilateral treaty arrangements, the Agency could gradually take over many of the functions of enforcement for such international arrangements as might require enforcement in the international media, and in this way expand its function and designation from that of an advisory agency to that of the single commanding International Environmental Authority which the international community is bound, at some point, to require. . . .

Europe Has Its Lake Eries *

The Rhine, like many great American rivers, degenerates into a polluted sewer as it flows to the sea.

At its source, its water is pure. Halfway to the sea it has picked up 24,000 undesirable organisms per cubic centimeter. But by the time it has run its course, the microbe population has jumped to two million per cc. This says nothing of the toxic chemicals it carries or of the occasional chemical spills that can kill millions of river fish.

In air pollution Paris rivals New York or Los Angeles. In one experiment, thirty-six volunteers stayed for three hours at the most polluted points in Paris. Carbon monoxide in their blood rose thirty per cent. The city has a daily fallout of ten tons of sulfuric acid, formed by sulfur products spewed into the atmosphere. Similar conditions prevail in many other European cities. Much could be done by cleaning up industry. But, as in America, automobiles are the chief culprit. Some sixty per cent of Europe's air pollution is laid to them.

Europe has its Lake Eries, too. The lake at Zurich, once clean and productive, "is now an evil-smelling muddy sewer," according to Professor R. Passino, director of the Water Research Institute at Rome. Many other European lakes face the same fate, he says.

Pollution is showing up along Europe's coasts. Some fish species have disappeared from accustomed grounds along the French Riviera. Professor Passino also cited cases along the coasts of Versilia, southern Tuscany, and Latium, where marine pollution is killing coastal pines. Long adapted to saltwater spray, the pines there now are dying where the spray hits them.   ROBERT C. COWEN
The Christian Science Monitor
February 25, 1970

CONFIDENTIAL

DEPARTMENT OF
POPULATION AND ENVIRONMENT

FIFTH ANNUAL REPORT TO THE PRESIDENT
JANUARY 1, 2000

Looking Backward
from 2000 A.D.

by PAUL R. EHRLICH

PAUL R. EHRLICH *is professor of biology and
director of graduate study for the department
of biological sciences at Stanford University. A
specialist in population biology, he is the author
of the best-selling paperback,* The Population
Bomb. *A new book written with his wife Anne
H. Ehrlich—*Population, Resources, Environment: Issues in Human Ecology—*has just been
published.*

SUMMARY

1. POPULATION: SIZE

The 1999 midyear population of the United States of North America was estimated to be 22.6 million, with a standard error of 3.2 million. The policy of special reproducer rations appears to have made significant inroads into the frequency of stillbirth, and child-health squads seem to be effectively reducing post-weaning child mortality. With the crude birth rate now standing at 30.7 and the death rate at 31.6, we are now clearly within striking distance of stabilizing our population. If present trends continue, the population will cease to decline early in 2001, and a slow rise in population size may be expected to commence thereafter. Approximately thirty-four per cent of the population now resides in SRU (Standard Reorganized Urban) Areas, and the redistribution program has returned to the inactive mode. The Division of Optimum Population is expected to recommend next year a program target of a stable population of thirty-two million by 2075.

2. POPULATION: QUALITY

The consequences of the release of radioactivity in the 1981 reactor disaster at the Seaborg plant, combined with the overall increase in environmental radioactivity permitted before the Gofman-Tamplin Act of 1976 restricted emissions, are still causing serious repercussions in our population. The leukemia rate is still 740 per cent higher than the 1960 base rate, and that of chondrodystrophic dwarfism is now 890 per cent of base. Estimates of the degree to which radiation is responsible for the present levels of embryonic, neonatal, infant, and childhood deaths are difficult to obtain because of confounding with nutritional effects and the disorganization of our medical apparatus. Similarly, it is still impossible to sort out the causative factors for the present high level of carcinomas of all types in all age groups, but a substantial portion is thought to result from radiation damage.

It is encouraging that surviving molecular biologists and human geneticists are now relocated, and that research and training are proceeding as well as can be expected. Efforts are, of course, being heavily concentrated on the problem of repair of radiation damage in DNA (the genetic material).

The genetic variability inventory is nearing completion. Preliminary results indicate that the reduction of population size has not resulted in serious loss. The heterogeneity of the American population is considered by many specialists to have been responsible for its high survival rate relative to that of many other overdeveloped countries. It is suggested that in your State of the System address you emphasize, in layman's terms, the critical role played by "minorities" in our survival. The level of racial tension is now lower than at any previous date in our history, and positive efforts should be made to eliminate such tension entirely.

3. POPULATION: HEALTH

It is clear that lowered population density is a primary factor in preventing a resurgence of Marburgvirus B. Another factor is the recovery of the average diet to 2400 calories per day, and the increase of the high quality protein ration to almost forty grams daily. Famine has been estimated to have been directly or indirectly responsible for sixty-five million American deaths in the decade 1980-1989; the chances of a substantial hunger component in the next decade is now judged to be very small, unless another dramatic change in the climate occurs.

In addition, of course, the continual improvement of the quality of the atmosphere since the Great Die-Off has resulted in a population much less weakened by circulatory and respiratory diseases, and will thus lessen mortality due to interactions between malnutrition and cardiovascular and respiratory disorders. In the past eighteen years the turbidity of the atmosphere at all reporting points has shown almost continual decline except in areas affected locally by uncontrolled forest fires and dust from unattended farm land. (Even such local effects have been almost non-existent since 1992.) Finally, the restoration of relatively pure water supplies in many areas has further improved the epidemiological situation, although nitrate levels remain unacceptable in some areas where ground water was badly polluted.

Radiation still seems to be a factor in the continued susceptibility of some of the population to Marburgvirus B and in continued low resistance to some other diseases. However, the level of chlorinated hydrocarbons stored in human body tissues has dropped until this factor is now thought to be negligible in lowering resistance. Remember that although about 125 million American deaths were attributed to Marburgvirus B during the Great Die-Off, it is clear that as many as sixty million of these would not have occurred if the population had not been weakened by environmental deterioration. Therefore the estimate of ten million deaths due to environmental problems other than famine and disease is undoubtedly too low.

Rumors that Marburgvirus A (the strain which first infected 30 laboratory workers in 1967, killing seven, and which was only prevented from becoming epidemic by a stroke of luck) has been causing deaths in Central African populations are unconfirmed, but the Immigration and Carrier Act of 1996 will probably provide protection for the population of the United States, if the presence of that strain in the human population is confirmed.

4. RESOURCES: FOOD

For the first time since these reports were initiated the Department can report progress on a broad front at restoring the productivity of American farms. The soil restoration program of the Department of Agriculture is now well out of the development stage, and trained extension workers are expected to be in contact with approximately twenty-five per cent of farmers working five acres or more during the next growing season. Acceptance of both humus building and integrated pest control techniques is extremely high in farmers who survived the disaster years of the mid-'80s and, of course, it will be even higher among the graduates of the new Federal Agricultural University. Monitoring of all agricultural inputs by the Department of Population and Environment has completely eliminated the abuses of the agri-business swindles of the 1970s. With care it should be possible to return the American diet to the 1960 nutritional base level by 2010, as programs developing satisfactory substitutes for dairy products and sea foods are showing remarkable progress.

Food distribution is now considerably more equitable than in the base year 1960, and considering the broad support of the population redistribution program and the rapid recovery of the national railways it is confidently predicted that serious dietary inequities will not occur in the foreseeable future.

5. RESOURCES: ENERGY

The Energy-Demand Control Act of 1998 has established the basis for rational utilization of the energy resources of the United States. In view of the great reduction in population size, fossil fuel supplies will be more than adequate (in combination with hydroelectric power) to sustain our economy over the next century. It is now estimated that Deuterium-He fusion will be operational, producing pollution-free power by 2050, which will allow about fifty years to complete the transition to all-electric power.

6. RESOURCES: MINERAL

Small population size, and continued availability of salvageable materials in Los Angeles and other cities

which have not been reoccupied, have greatly eased
the pressure on our reserves of non-renewable resources.
The projected non-renewable resource crisis is now about
100 years into the future, although, if international
trade is not firmly reestablished in the next decade,
shortages of certain materials such as industrial dia-
monds may be serious. We must emphasize that national and international planning for resource husband-
ry and substitution must be organized as soon as possible. We must not let the lessons of the '70s and '80s
go unheeded. Needless to say, the planning of the Stable
Economy Commission must go ahead with all deliberate
speed.

7. ENVIRONMENT

As indicated above, air and water quality have now
both exceeded the 1960 base level by a considerable
amount. Movement of chlorinated hydrocarbon residues
into oceanic sinks is now estimated to have reached
eighty-three per cent of completion. The Department
concurs, however, with estimates of Eastbloc monitoring
stations that the restoration of oceanic productivity is
problematical. Fears of oxygen depletion are still present in certain segments of the population, and it is
essential that they be reassured. Large terrestrial areas
have reverted to green plants since the Die-Off, and
even if oceanic ecosystems cannot be reestablished for
several centuries no significant oxygen shortage is
anticipated.

Whether or not weather patterns will eventually return to those of the early part of the Twentieth Century cannot be determined at this time. Those few atmospheric physicists who survived the Die-Off have not
reached a consensus on the exact cause of the jet
stream shifts of 1978-84. Much more basic research on
turbulent flow will be necessary before any attempt to
reestablish previous patterns by artificial means can be
made, and any such program is clearly beyond our cur-

rent capability. While a rapid spontaneous return is conceivable, it would clearly be foolish to plan on that basis. It is important to remember also that a *rapid* return now would cause serious disruption in the new agricultural programs which have been established, and might result in a return of famine.

MAJOR RECOMMENDATIONS

1. The continuation of present pronatalist policies will be necessary for the foreseeable future. It is important, however, that the public be continually reminded that the fundamental role of this Department is not to encourage population growth, but to *regulate* the size of the population for the benefit of all our citizens. The public should be prepared for the institution of anti-natalist policies whenever conditions require them.

2. The Congress should immediately ratify the population convention of the United Nations World System Treaty.

3. Increased support of research in molecular biology, even in the face of extreme fiscal difficulties, is necessary in view of the severe genetic and metabolic difficulties faced by our population. The need to rebuild this area of science is made doubly urgent by the possible presence in the human population of Marburgvirus A and by the persistence of foci of Marburgvirus B in spite of the universal distribution of the Hsui vaccine. The reasons for the partial failure of the vaccine are as yet undetermined, but a larger cadre of trained scientists is clearly needed to help with this and related problems. Some slowdown in training programs of the National Ecology Institute could be accepted and the

funds shifted to molecular biology. Ecology is now recruiting more talented students than can be usefully employed.

4. Appeals for loosening of restrictions under the Immigration and Carrier Act should be ignored for at least one more year.

5. No changes in the activities of the Department of Agriculture are recommended except in the Wheatlands Holding Unit. In view of the small probability of weather changes permitting the Wheatlands Reserve to be cultivated in the near future, the funds expended on this unit would better be reallocated to the South Coastal unit.

6. The remaining restrictions on the use of internal combustion engines in agriculture may now be safely lifted, with of course the provision that pre-disaster leaded fuel stocks remain under bond.

7. As the climatic changes of the last quarter century appear to be more or less permanent, it is recommended that a new climatic base be established as of this date.

8. The Department recommends that the President's Human Survival Medal be awarded posthumously to Dr. John W. Gofman and Dr. Arthur R. Tamplin. These scientists, while employed by the Lawrence Radiation Laboratory, which was supported by Atomic Energy Commission (AEC) funds, challenged the AEC guidelines for permissible levels of radiation exposure. Their courage and determination in the face of ill-founded bureaucratic opposition from the AEC eventually led to the landmark Federal Radiation Emissions Act of 1976, popularly known as the Gofman-Tamplin Act. As you know, untold human suffering has been avoided because of the enforcement of the act. The Department feels that further recognition of Gofman and Tamplin at this time will drive home to our new government agencies the need both for extreme care in dealing with environmental problems, and your direct concern for the rights of individuals within those agencies to be heard.

CONCLUSIONS

This is the first report of the Department in which the prognosis for the United States is mildly positive. In spite of this, a cautionary note must be added. In the national press there has been some comment to the effect that the environmental and public health disasters of the 1970s and 1980s were the result of "bad luck" or "Acts of God." As you know, Mr. President, if we had any luck it was good—for with bad luck the famines, disease, and competition for resources could have precipitated a thermonuclear war. It is only because most of the physical apparatus and records of our culture survived intact that recovery to the present point has been possible. We now can say with certainty that a major thermonuclear war in the 1970s or 1980s would have ended civilization permanently.

The Department urges you to remind our citizens that all of the trends leading to disaster were clear twenty years before the end came, and that we and the rest of mankind did nothing substantive to avert it. As a single example, the vulnerability of the world population to epidemic disease, due to large population size (overcrowding), hunger, and environmental deterioration was repeatedly pointed out by scientists. No substantial action was taken to correct the situation by a nation addicted to economic growth and ignorant of the limits of technology.

The cost of inaction, apathy, and unwarranted optimism has been the payment of nearly four billion human lives over a fifteen year period—and we are still paying. We cannot permit a repetition of such a disaster. Mr. President, it is imperative that this generation and those to follow be kept mindful of mankind's recent history.

> Respectfully submitted,
> (Signed)
> L. PAGE KENNEDY
> Secretary

When the People Speak Up

An Epilogue
by the Editors
of *The Progressive*

Although the crisis of survival is man-made, the chances of survival and the achievement of a balance between man and nature are also in man's hands. Pollution and destruction have been the trademarks of our lust for profit and growth, but in recent years there have been signs—slight, to be sure—that an enlightened populace, mobilized for political action, can halt if not reverse the poisoning of our environment. We have brought together below a few examples of modest success achieved by an aroused people confronted by environmental challenge. There are many others of comparable character.

San Francisco Bay

For more than a century man has been ravaging the San Francisco Bay area, a fifty-mile long chain of inland seas comprising òne of the world's most beautiful regions, and one endowed with great natural resources. Since 1850, more than forty per cent of the Bay has been filled for industry and homebuilding. A few years ago an Army Corps of Engineers' report disclosed that two-thirds of the Bay was less than twelve feet deep, and "susceptible to reclamation" or further filling, and that half of this area belonged to private owners or local governments.

In the 1950s and 1960s, one shoreline community after another announced plans to expand their land areas into the Bay. Then the city of Berkeley proposed to double its size by filling 2,000 acres of the Bay.

What happened next was an inspiring example of the power of an angry citizenry when aroused by a ruthless assault upon the environment. Mrs. Clark Kerr, wife of the then president of the University of California, and two friends enlisted the aid of the Sierra Club, the Save the Redwoods League, the Audubon Society, and other groups to save the Bay. The Save San Francisco Bay Association was formed and with the support of thousands of citizens defeated the Berkeley Bay fill plan by making it a local election issue.

From this success, the Association went on to a broader approach. It lined up some key leaders of the California legislature and with massive citizen support succeeded in getting a bill passed that created a Bay Conservation and Development Commission to explore ways of developing San Francisco Bay's maximum values without harming its scenic or recreational potential. A key provision of the law prohibits any new fill during the Commission's three-year study without a public hearing and Commission approval.

There was influential opposition to the legislation

but Association members turned out en masse at Sacramento when the bill was before the legislature, flooded lawmakers with petitions, letters, telephone calls, and telegrams. Some inventive Oakland citizens mailed small bags of sand to their legislators with tags that read: "You'll wonder where the water went, if you fill the Bay with sediment."

The Commission's report, submitted in January 1969, declared that the Bay must not be considered "ordinary real estate" but must be protected as an asset belonging to the people of the area, state, and nation. Powerful interests are lobbying against the Commission's position, but the citizens who halted the real estate developers and the industrial demand for land fills realize that while they have won a major battle, the war to save the Bay still goes on.

New York State

Last year New York State citizens swept aside familiar arguments that environmental controls might cut into industry's profits, slow down highway building projects, or, in some way, alter the American way of Progress at Any Price; they voted an amendment to their constitution that gave the state government new powers and responsibility to stop air and water pollution, end unnecessary noise, and protect wetlands, shorelines, and other priceless resources from reckless development and exploitation.

The campaign began with efforts to elect delegates to the state's constitutional convention in 1967 who were committed to strong environmental provisions. The amendment failed that year along with the rest of the proposed new constitution. But in 1968, the proponents were back at the legislature with the proposed constitutional change. It passed, and in 1969, it passed again, meeting New York's requirement of approval by two legislatures before submission to the people. In last November's statewide general election, voters approved the amendment by five to one, the greatest margin for any constitutional change in the history of New York, and the amendment was adopted.

Other states—Illinois, Massachusetts, Colorado, and Maryland among them—are now embarked on similar efforts. And at the national level, Senator Gaylord Nelson, Wisconsin Democrat, introduced a one paragraph amendment to the U.S. Constitution in January that reads: "Every person has the inalienable right to a decent environment. The United States and every State shall guarantee that right." Given widespread support by citizens, such a right could well become a fundamental doctrine of the society within a few years and a part of the U.S Constitution.

The Everglades

In 1934, Congress established 1.4-million-acre Everglades National Park to be "protected in perpetuity" as a unique subtropical wilderness. But in an age where the most enduring mark of American "Progress" threatens to be a ravaged continent, the Everglades wilderness predictably faced a tenuous foothold in rapidly developing south Florida. Planning big, the Miami area's Dade County Port Authority last year was scheduling construction of the world's largest airport—at a cost of $250-$300 million. The massive project was to occupy a thirty-nine square-mile site only six miles from the park.

A study for the Department of the Interior pointed out the folly in graphic terms. Bluntly put, the airport-associated air, water, and noise pollution, and the massive urban development the airport would bring would destroy the national park. The Department of Transportation—without consulting Interior—had contributed nearly a million dollars toward construction of the airport.

When the increasingly environment-sensitive public learned—through widespread press reports—of the danger to this world renowned park, outrage began to sweep the land. One Senator received 400 letters of support after a national television program mentioned him as being concerned about the situation. National conservation groups formed an Everglades coalition, and in a skillful educational effort convinced public officials from Florida to the White House that the proposed airport site could not be tolerated. Congressional hearings pointed out the tragic irony of one taxpayer-supported project, the park, being threatened by another Federal aid project, the airport.

Early this year, the massive Congressional, environmentalist, and citizen effort to prevent the park's destruction led to a White House-backed agreement with the Dade County Port Authority that a new, environmentally-safe site would be found for the big jetport, and that a pilot-training strip already constructed at the Everglades site would operate under environmental safeguards and would be abandoned when the new airport is put in operation.

Another major danger to the park—a U.S. Army Corps of Engineers "water conservation" project that threatens to choke off the vital natural water supply through the Everglades—is still unresolved.

Grand Canyon

Another threat to America's scarce wilderness—this time to the Grand Canyon—was halted in 1967 after a four-year national debate. The issue was raised by a proposal to build two large hydroelectric dams on the stretch of the Colorado River that runs through the Grand Canyon in Northern Arizona. The dams, backed by a powerful coalition of Southwest power and water interests, would have been a massive intrusion into the Grand Canyon, altering forever a natural area that has been held in awe by Americans for generations.

A four-year campaign by conservation organizations and millions of individuals persuaded Congress to reject both the Grand Canyon dams. The campaign was accompanied by full page newspaper advertisements that stimulated a letter writing campaign which the Senators and Congressmen—on the receiving end—said was unprecedented in its volume and intensity of protest.

Lake Washington

Seattle's Lake Washington, a beautiful residential and recreation mecca for a growing metropolis, was gravely polluted until just a few years ago by, of all things, *treated* sewage. Twenty million gallons a day, all treated at secondary (two stage) levels, were pouring into the twenty-two-mile long lake from the ten sewage plants servicing the Lake Washington area.

The community became aware of the lake's deterioration in the early 1950s, but a decade later, pollution was still continuing to ravage this magnificent body of water. In large part, the culprit was phosphorus, an element that can fertilize plants in a lake or river until the water is murky and stinking with recreation-destroying algae and other signs of decay. Secondary treatment of sewage does a poor job of removing the persistent phosphorus compounds that are rapidly increasing in our environment because of—among other things—heavy detergent use.

In the late 1950s, the first step was taken toward what was to become a dramatic success in halting the destruction of Lake Washington. A seventy-five-man committee was formed which quickly became the nucleus of a tremendous citizen push to clean up the lake.

The state legislature was prevailed upon, in 1957, to pass a bill that led to the establishment a year later of a metropolitan council with the power and the resources to tackle the problem. Engineering studies pointed the way, and a comprehensive plan was adopted for a vast new treatment system that would direct all sewage away from the lake.

Since then, municipal bonds supported by the voters have financed construction of more than $140 million in treatment facilities. The metropolitan council will finish a year ahead of the ten-year deadline set for completion of the massive first stage of the cleanup.

The improvement in the lake seems incredible. Recently, there were reports that, for the first time in years, one could see the lake bottom in sixteen to twenty feet of water. Last summer there was only one serious algae infestation, which meant that people could swim again without being coated with slime. The phosphorus count was down to almost a third of its previous levels. Because people acted in time, even if belatedly, Lake Washington is on the road to recovery.

New Orleans

Modern man not only scars the beauty of nature, he frequently mars or destroys the priceless cultural creations left him by his ancestors. Industrial development, for example, is causing Venice to sink into the sea and is corroding the surfaces of its ancient architectural treasures. And all over America, cultural pollution has replaced old and beautiful buildings with new and ugly ones—or with miles of freeways and acres of parking lots.

But in New Orleans, environmentalists scored a victory last year. When plans were announced for an expressway that would have plowed through the city's *Vieux Carre,* the historic French quarter, and separated it from the Mississippi River waterfront, they argued that the commercial benefits were far outweighed by the ugly mark the expressway would leave on the historic waterfront. Although local highway and planning agencies already had approved the route, the U.S. Department of Transportation supported the environmentalists' contention and denied Federal highway aid for the proposed riverfront expressway.

National Forests

Environmentalists sometimes are startled by the nature of their allies on a given issue. Thus a successful lobbying effort against passage of a bill to permit increased logging in national forests was led by the Sierra Club and included such diverse groups as the United Auto Workers, the Audubon Society—and the National Rifle Association, the nation's chief lobby against gun control laws.

In spite of pressure from the timber industry and Nixon Administration support, the logging bill was defeated in the House 228 to 150. Titled the National Forest Timber Conservation and Management Act, the measure, opponents said, provided no safeguards to prevent adverse effects on watershed protection, wildlife habitat, and recreation opportunities in forests.

Student Power

The brightest hope for progress on the environmental front rests with American youth who this year have enrolled by the tens of thousands in local, state, and national campaigns to restore and preserve the quality of life. In the best traditions of the democratic processes they are educating the citizenry on environmental needs, supporting political action to reduce pollution of air and water, and campaigning for conservation of scarce land resources.

Some examples of student power in action on behalf of these constructive objectives are cited in Gladwin Hill's article. A few others:

¶ Students at Thomas School, a girls' high school in Rowayton, Connecticut, invited public officials to attend a "political breakfast" to discuss the threatened obliteration of a marsh by land developers. The officials said little could be done to save the wetland. The girls wrote every member of the state legislature, campaigned with letters, flyers, and with "Protect Your Environment" buttons to rally opposition to the proposal to eliminate the wetland. Their efforts contributed to the passage of a bill by the state legislature which saved the marsh. At least fifteen other high schools and five colleges have adopted their button and are now active on environmental issues.

¶ When students and faculty at a State University of New York learned that a road, parking facilities, and a sports field were being constructed on campus in the middle of a fifty-acre natural area, more than a hundred of them marched out to the site and halted the bulldozers and trucks. The ad hoc ecology group met with the university administration and won these major concessions: It was agreed that no parking lot or playing field would be built in the area, that road construction would be halted and a new route sought, and that the board of trustees would be requested by the school administration to set aside the fifty-acre marsh and thirty surrounding acres as a natural preserve. On top of all this, the university president agreed to request the faculty senate to set up a standing committee on the university environment.

¶ The rapid increase in the use of throw-away bottles and cans has made scarce space in municipal dumps even scarcer. Concerned about the problem, University of Wisconsin students provided leadership in developing public support for a proposed city ordinance which, if enacted by the Madison City Council, would outlaw the use of all sorts of non-degradable containers—aluminum beer cans, non-returnable bottles, and the like. Although the suggested ordinance would not take effect for several years, discussion of this pioneer measure, which is likely to be proposed in other cities, could force bottlers, the packaging industry, and manufacturers of goods sold in non-degradable containers to step up the search for degradable materials.

As the foregoing examples suggest, aroused and dedicated citizens can achieve success in combating some assaults upon the environment. But the struggle ahead will not be an easy one. Far from it. For the forces which contribute, knowingly or unwittingly, to the deterioration of land, air, water, and the quality of life itself are enormously powerful.

Through education, persuasion, and the power of public opinion these forces may be induced to institute reforms, as, indeed, some are now doing. But they are not likely to make the basic changes so urgently required to save our environment until government at all levels—national, state, and local—not only enacts a new and fundamental program of public regulation, but also enforces with stern vigilance the many existing laws which have been flouted for years by corporations, individuals, and many government agencies themselves.

Government will be called upon to be the great equalizer in the citizens' struggle to preserve a livable world. That means citizens will be organizing politically to secure federal, state, and local environmental legislation on a scale far greater than anything achieved so far. This process has barely begun.

Environmental scientists repeatedly point out that basic decisions reached and acted upon by the public

Bibliography

PAPERBACK

Abrams, Charles. *The City Is The Frontier*. New York: Harper & Row, 1965.

Bates, Marston. *The Forest and the Sea*. New York: Random House, Inc., 1960.

Battan, Louis J. *The Unclean Sky*. New York: Doubleday Anchor Books.

Borgstrom, Georg. *The Hungry Planet*. New York: The Macmillan Company, 1965.

Boulding, Kenneth. *A Reconstruction of Economics*. New York: John Wiley & Sons, Inc., 1950. See especially Chapter 1, "An Ecological Introduction."

Boulding, Kenneth. *The Meaning of the Twentieth Century*. New York: Harper & Row, 1965.

Brower, David, ed. *Voices for the Wilderness*. New York: Ballantine Books, 1969.

Carson, Rachel. *Silent Spring*. Boston: Fawcett World, 1962.

Commoner, Barry. *Science and Survival*. New York: Viking Compass, 1968.

De Bell, Garrett. *The Environmental Handbook*. New York: Ballantine Books, 1969.

Edelson, Edward and Fred Warshofsky. *Poisons in the Air*. New York: Pocket Books.

Ehrlich, Paul R. *The Population Bomb*. New York: Ballantine Books, 1969.

Ewald, William R., Jr., ed. *Environment and Change: The Next Fifty Years*. Bloomington: Indiana University Press, 1968.

Forbes, R. J. *The Conquest of Nature: Technology and Its Consequences*. New York: New American Library, 1968.

Frisch, Karl von. *Man and the Living World*. New York: Harvest, 1949, 1962.

Galbraith, John K. "How Much Should a Country Consume?" In *Perspectives in Conservation*, edited by Henry Jarrett. Resources for the Future, 1958.

Goldman, Marshall, ed. *Controlling Pollution: The Economics of a Cleaner America*. Englewood Cliffs, N.J.: Prentice-Hall, Inc., 1967.

Hauser, Philip M. *The Population Dilemma*. (A Spectrum Book.) Englewood Cliffs, N.J.: Prentice-Hall, Inc., 1963.

Henderson, Lawrence J. *The Fitness of the Environment*. Boston: The Beacon Press, 1958.

Hogan, Elizabeth and Richard Curtis. *Perils of the Peaceful Atom*. New York: Ballantine Books.

Jacobs, Jane. *The Death and Life of Great American Cities*. New York: Vintage Books.

Leinwand, Gerald, gen. ed. *Air and Water Pollution*. New York: Washington Square Press, 1969.

Leopold, Aldo. *A Sand County Almanac*. New York: Oxford University Press, 1968.

Lord, Russell. *The Care of the Earth*. New York: Mentor Books, 1964.

Marx, Wesley. *The Frail Ocean*. New York: Doubleday Anchor Books, 1967.

Mitchell, John G. with Constance L. Stallings, eds. *Ecotactics: The Sierra Club Handbook for Environment Activists*. New York: Pocket Books, 1970. Foreword by Ralph Nader.

Mumford, Lewis. *The Urban Prospect*. New York: Harcourt, Brace & World, 1969.

Osborn, Fairfield. *Our Plundered Planet*. Boston: Little, Brown and Company.

Paddock, William and Paul. *Famine—1975*. Boston: Little, Brown and Company, 1967.

Rienow, Robert and Leona. *Moment in the Sun: A Report on the Deteriorating Quality of the American Environment*. New York: Ballantine Books, 1969.

Rudd, Robert L. *Pesticides and the Living Landscape*. Madison: University of Wisconsin Press, 1964.

Shepard, Paul and D. McKinley, eds. *The Subversive Science: Essays Toward an Ecology of Man*. Boston: Houghton Mifflin Company.

Storer, John H. *The Web of Life*. New York: Signet Books, 1966.

U.S. Congress. Senate Committee on Public Works. 1965. *Waste, Management Research and Environmental Quality Management*. Washington: U.S. Senate.

Hard Cover

Benarde, Melvin A. *Our Precarious Habitat*. New York: W. W. Norton & Company.

Borgstrom, Georg. *Too Many. A Study of Earth's Biological Limitation*. The Macmillan Company, 1969.

Borland, Hal, ed. *Our Natural World*. New York: J. B. Lippincott, 1969.

Ciriacy-Wantrup, S. V. and J. J. Parsons, eds. *Natural Resources: Quality & Quantity*. Berkeley: University of California Press, 1966.

Darling, F. Fraser and John Milton, eds. *Future Environments of North America*. New York: Natural History Press, 1966.

Douglas, William O. *Wilderness Bill of Rights*. Boston: Little, Brown and Company, 1965.

Ehrlich, Paul R. and Anne H. *Population, Resources, Environment: Issues in Human Ecology*. San Francisco: W. H. Freeman, 1970.

Graham, Frank, Jr. *Since Silent Spring*. Boston: Houghton Mifflin Company.

Hardin, Garrett, ed. *Population, Evolution, and Birth Control*. San Francisco: W. H. Freeman, 1969.

Hunter, Beatrice Trum. *Gardening Without Poisons*. Boston: Houghton Mifflin Company, 1964.

Joffee, Joyce. *Conservation: Maintaining the Natural Balance*. New York: Natural History Press.

Mayer, Albert. *The Urgent Future: People, Housing, City, Region*. New York: McGraw-Hill Book Company, 1967.

Milne, Lorus and Margery. *The Balance of Nature*. New York: Alfred A. Knopf, Inc., 1960.

Mowbray, A. Q. *The Road to Ruin*. New York: J. B. Lippincott, 1969.

Murphy, Earl F. *Governing Nature*. Chicago: Quadrangle Books, Inc., 1967.

Rudofsky, Bernard. *Streets for People: A Primer for Americans*. Garden City, N.Y.: Doubleday & Company.

Russell, Franklin. *Searchers at the Gulf*. New York: W. W. Norton & Company, 1970.

Stewart, George R. *Not So Rich as You Think*. Boston: Houghton Mifflin Company, 1968.

White, Gilbert, ed. *Water, Health and Society*. Bloomington: Indiana University Press, 1969.

Whyte, William H. *The Last Landscape*. Garden City, N.Y.: Doubleday & Company, 1968.

ADDITIONAL WORKS OF INTEREST

Caldwell, Lynton K., ed. *Science Technology and Public Policy: A Selected and Annotated Bibliography*. Available through Program of Advanced Studies in Science Technology and Society, Department of Government, Indiana University, Bloomington, Indiana.

Crowe, Philip Kingsland. *World Wildlife: The Last Stand*. New York: Charles Scribner's Sons.

Davies, Clarence. *The Politics of Pollution*. New York: Pegasus.

Helfrich, Harold W., Jr., ed. *The Environmental Crisis: Man's Struggle to Live With Himself*. New Haven: Yale University Press.

Higbee, Edward. *A Question of Priorities*. New York: William Morrow & Co., Inc.

Moore, John A., ed. *Science For Society, A Bibliography*. Forthcoming. Washington: American Association For the Advancement of Science.

A Sourcebook on Population. Washington: Population Reference Bureau. 1969.
